THE LIFE CHEST

INTRIGUE, ADVENTURE and WISDOM

THE LIFE CHEST

INTRIGUE, ADVENTURE and WISDOM

BY KIM YOST

With Terie Spencer,
Agata Wysokinski and Donna Yost
Illustrations by Kristen Trawczynski

Life 2000 Ltd.
1583 Heronwood Court
Bloomfield Hills, Michigan 48302

Library of Congress Control Number: 2014956427

ISBN-13: 978-0-578-15254-7

First printing, November 2014

Printed in Canada

Contents

Foreword

We were so pleased when Andrew Cohen accepted the opportunity to write our foreword. Andrew played a special role in the launch of the original life chest project in the year 2000 when he took on a licensing agreement to sell life chests throughout North America. He is a personal friend of both Donna and I. We have enjoyed our relationship and his constant encouragement of the life chest project over the years.

Andrew Cohen

President

HUMANTOUCH.com

If you sit down for a conversation with Kim Yost you will see right away his passionate about a lot of things:

- Sharing life learning through his *Pumptitude* trilogy, to help people of all ages and stations make a great life. The stories and anecdotes in Kim's motivational books grab you, providing strong doses of common sense and positivity that will pep up both your business and personal life.

- Encouraging people to keep a Life Chest. "What is a Life Chest?" you may ask. It is a place to store memories; keepsakes that might otherwise be relegated to a shoebox. Besides being a safe and secure home for memories, it is a repository for future goals and an inspiration to live your best life in the present.

These two passions have come together in the writing of this book, *The Life Chest*. Kim's vision was to embed his favorite learning from the *Pumptitude* books into an action-filled, compelling story that creates a history and background for the Life Chest tradition.

Many inspiring stories are in the pages of the *Pumptitude* series, both from Kim Yost's life and from businesspeople and celebrities who have been inspired by his ideas. One special story was written by Donna Yost as an Appendix to *Maximum Pumptitude*. It is a fable about a young man in the future whose life is changed when he is introduced to *Pumptitude* and the concept of the Life Chest. This story became the Prologue for *The Life Chest*.

Kim and his team of collaborators take the reader to ancient China, where the story follows the adventures of Marco Polo. Marco builds the precursor to the Life Chest, which he calls the dynasty chest, and gives it to his Nepalese Sherpa guide. The story continues through the guide's descendants, as they hand down Marco Polo's dynasty chest and create their own, while benefiting from the learning imparted by the treasures and keepsakes held in the chests.

Finally, the story comes full circle as the young man Josh, discovers a secret about the original dynasty chest and travels back to China for an adventure of a lifetime.

Kim's enthusiasm for the adventure that is life itself shines through in *The Life Chest*. It is a wonderful combination of an exciting story with memorable characters -- a reminder of the learning that can make a great life. The wisdom of reflection is the theme of this book and you will find yourself captivated by the adventure as it unfolds.

The mystery of a *Life Chest* is alluring; every person has a story to share with future generations. Past lessons come alive by the content in one's chest. I am confident that you will enjoy this story so much that you will want to keep the book in your own *Life Chest*.

Introduction

Why was I compelled to write our fourth book, *The Life Chest*? This is a great question, given that the first three books took our team almost a full year each to complete.

The answer is simple. I needed to tell *The Life Chest* story. One reason was to give credit to so many who have made *The Life Chest* dream a reality. Another reason was to share the amazing accomplishments of my wife Donna and her single-minded focus to revive *The Life Chest* and its mission. Her passion and vision for *The Life Chest* is simply what the whole Life Chest movement is about! She lives in the present, putting things into her Life Chest every day. She lives in the future by creating it. She is building a legacy for our family, and living *The Life Chest* philosophy so that everyone can learn from her example.

The Life Chest philosophy is beautifully expressed by *The Life Chest* logo, created by Donna. When she travelled to China for the first time Donna got the idea to make a logo with the look of an ancient Chinese coin, a treasure she found in a Shanghai market. The designs and symbols on that coin were the inspiration behind the significant story of the logo. *Life Chests* emphasize the past, present, and future, and the logo reflects this as follows:

- The Chinese characters, which mean *forever remember*, symbolize the past and together they stand for *eternity* and signify *longevity*.

- The wings represent time travel, connecting our past, present and future.

- The incomplete infinity symbol is the keystone of the logo. *The Life Chest* team participated in the development of a logo, which would represent the untold stories of millions. An infinity symbol represents eternity, but the *The Life Chest* infinity symbol says more. The dots in the symbol represent the unique

moments in your life today. By creating your own
stories, you "connect the dots." Preserving your stories
in *The Life Chest* ensures a lasting legacy.

This story has been in the making since 1983, when my life
was changed by an experience like no other. My personal story
is told in *The Life Chest*, and is wrapped in exciting historical
fiction, which details the creation and history of *The Life Chest*
itself. This project has been an all-consuming creative effort,
and I hope you will enjoy reading it as much as we have enjoyed
writing it.

The Life Chest is filled with life lessons from the *Pumptitude*
trilogy that are intended to educate, inspire and motivate.
I realized years ago that storytelling is by far the best way to
share knowledge. We pray that not only will you enjoy our
storytelling but that this book will inspire you to obtain a life
chest of your own and experience the magic it will bring to you
and yours, now and in future generations.

Enjoy the adventure of a lifetime!

Kim Yost

Dedication

I dedicate this book to my wife Donna for her unfailing vision and passion for *The Life Chest*. She has been an incredible inspiration to our entire team and I throughout this book writing experience. She accompanied us to China to complete our research and assisted in the telling of the story. If one phrase could describe her, it would be "energy personified."

As the CEO of Art Van, the Midwest's number one furniture dealer, I keep a hectic schedule, to put it mildly. Those familiar with my *Pumptitude* books will understand when I say that I have devoted every Schmonday for several months to the completion of this book.

I would like to express my sincere appreciation and give applause to our life chest book team who made *The Life Chest* possible by virtue of their tireless work- and putting up with me, too. Terie, Agata, and Kristin worked well as a team. They have their creative DNA all over this book, and through their involvement have created their own legacy. It has been a joy for all of us to share our talents and energy.

Donna Yost

Acknowledgments

Several people have been instrumental in making the life chest idea come to fruition. Two in particular stand out. The first is Bill Comrie, who, as you will discover in the pages of this book, contributed motivational, emotional, and financial support to the original life chest project. Second is Mr. Art Van Elslander. He helped kick off the relaunch of the life chest with his constant encouragement as well as giving Donna her first purchase order to sell life chests inside Art Van Furniture stores. Both these gentlemen were featured in the original *Pumptitude* book and have been dear friends for decades. Isn't it interesting how the life chest brings so many of us together in ways we would never have imagined?

Terie Spencer, ghostwriter

With an MFA in Theater Directing, Terie has directed close to 50 plays and authored several as well. She approaches all her writing with a theatrical eye and a keen ear for dialogue.

Agata Wysokinski, project manager

Agata works with *The Life Chest* in many capacities, from social media and marketing to the management and publishing of this book. She enjoys design but really loves nature photography and fashion.

Kristen Trawczynski, illustrator

Kristen is an illustrator and graduate of the Kendall College of Art and Design. She spent her childhood doodling all over her homework and never really stopped.

One Final "Brill"

Agata, Kristen and I would like to specially acknowledge Terie's writing skills. Her ability to capture our story and creatively build on it earned her several "brills" (short for brilliant) from us all throughout the process. She is amazing!

Prologue

A Life Chest—and Life Changes—for Josh

Josh sighed in relief as the door slid shut. He felt a little guilty escaping to the study, away from his granddaughter's birthday party. But a bunch of kids hopped up on sugar weren't gonna miss Grandpa if he stole away for a few minutes, he figured. April loved having her birthday parties at Grandpa and Grandma's house. Josh and his wife Leah enjoyed it too, but when a couple of April's rowdier friends started popping balloons, he had to take a break. It took him a minute to remember what year it was—2151? Yeah. He was seventy years old, so it was about forty years since the last time somebody had tried to shoot him. That was quite a while ago, but anything that sounded remotely like a gunshot still made him jump.

Josh shook his head to clear it, took a deep breath and a stretch, and settled in the easy chair next to his life chest. He ran his hand absentmindedly over its lid as he looked around for a zinepad. There was nothing within reach, and nothing worth the effort of getting out of his comfortable chair for. So as he'd done countless times before, Josh turned to the chest and opened the lid. Who needs a magazine to pass the time when you've got a life chest? Josh smiled to himself. A thirtieth anniversary vid from Leah, a crayon self-portrait by April, a Chinese coin from the Han Dynasty, and a ten-years-of-service award from his first job passed through his hands, along with the memories they contained.

Josh had just picked up a 3D photosim of his cousin Bernie when the door beeped. He saw April on the comm screen, pushed the button to open the door, and his granddaughter peeked in.

"Grandpa? Are you okay? Can I come in?"

"Sure, honey. I just wanted to sit down for a few minutes. Don't mind me. Go back and have fun."

"Oh, everybody's finishing cake and now they're singing karaoke. What are you looking at?"

Grandpa Josh and April explore Josh's life chest

April moved closer, climbed onto Josh's lap, and peeked into the chest. "Wow, your life chest is pretty full! Mine only has my baby photosims in it so far."

Josh laughed. "Well, I'm old! There's a lot of living stored up in there! And you're not much more than a baby, kiddo. You only got your life chest today!" He teasingly tousled his granddaughter's hair, knowing she hated it when he mussed up her "do".

"Grandpa, cut it out!" April laughed too as she pushed his hand away and hopped off his lap. "And I'm not a baby! I'm eight! I was born way back in 2143!"

"I know." Josh reassured the frowning little girl. "You're just growing up too fast for me, Blossom."

Hearing her nickname made April smile. "You always call me Blossom. Is that why you got me the pretty red chest with the flowers on it?"

"The Zen Blossom chest? Uh-huh. It reminded me of you. Now if you want to fill that chest, you better get back to the party and make some more memories to put in it! Is your dad recording the party?"

"Yup. But I want a story first. Tell me about that picture, Grandpa," she said, pointing.

"This one? Bernie and me? That's going to take more than one story, Blossom. But I've told you about Bernie before. Best friend I ever had. Saved my life more than once." Josh shook his head and couldn't help grinning. "OK, in this picture, we had just—"

"April!" Meg's voice interrupted what had promised to be an exciting but lengthy story. "Dad, is April in here?"

"Right here, Mom. I was checking on Grandpa."

"I'm sure Grandpa's just fine," said Meg, with a knowing smile for her dad. "You'll have to get a story out of him later. It's almost time for the kids to go home, so you'd better come in the family room. You don't want to be rude to your guests."

"Okay." April skipped across the room and turned back as she reached the door. "Grandpa? Thanks for the life chest. I love it!" And she was off, yelling "Can I sing next?" as she ran down the hall.

"*Are* you all right, Dad?" asked Meg hesitantly. She knew her dad didn't like to be fussed over, but a daughter can't help worrying sometimes.

"Heck, yes! Go back to the karaoke party. You're probably missing some great performances!"

Meg laughed as she pushed the button to close the door. "I'm sure. Good thing you just got new soundproofing!"

Picking up the photosim again, Josh promised himself to contact Bernie later that night. It would be great to catch up a little and thank him for April's gift. As he looked at Bernie's infectious grin, Josh thought about how much of his life chest, and his life, had been filled with and influenced by his cousin. That geeky kid whom Josh couldn't stand when they first met! Who would have thought? With a sigh, Josh admitted to himself that *he* was not exactly the most likeable guy when he showed up at his aunt and uncle's that first day. That day—what was it? Fifty years ago? Yep, to the month. August of 2101. He remembered it like it was yesterday, but not because it was such a great day. To be honest, it had started out rotten.

Josh, 19 years old and behind bars again

Late that morning, Josh had waited for his mom to come get him. He figured she would be pretty mad. Who wouldn't be, picking up their nineteen-year-old son from jail? But she was taking forever! Probably doing it on purpose to make him sweat. Josh paced back and forth in the holding room, getting madder and more frustrated. He slumped angrily in a chair. Yeah, there were some B&Es on his record—so what? He had an alibi for last night, but that hadn't done any good. Somebody said his name, and the cops hauled him in along with all the other "usual suspects". He told them he'd been with Leah yesterday, not at the sporting goods store that was robbed. They couldn't reach Leah to confirm it until morning, so Josh spent the night in a cell. I bet they wish they could just leave me in here to rot, he thought. Maybe my mom wishes that too. Josh listened for a door opening or a voice coming his way. Silence.

The law had nothing on him this time, but the trouble he *was* in was not the usual petty theft or drunk and disorderly. It was worse. He and Leah had scraped together just enough money for her to go to the clinic. That's where they were yesterday. Neither of them could bear to say the word abortion, but that's what it was. And it was done. Now everything felt wrong. He felt so distant from Leah—she didn't talk all the way back to her house. I don't know what else we could have done, thought Josh in despair. Leah wanted to finish her senior year. Josh had given up on high school, but it would be good if one of them had a diploma. And Leah was smart enough to go to college. Maybe someday. I'll find a job, and she can go to school, Josh thought. If I can even find a job. If she even still wants to be with me. He dropped his head in his hands. Or maybe I'll just live up to everybody's expectations and move on to grand theft auto. The bitterness rose in Josh's throat. He stood up, kicked the folding chair and spat into the corner in one angry motion.

"Hey!" A guard's face appeared in the door's small window. "Knock that off unless you wanna stay another night. Your ride's here." Josh picked up the chair, slammed it down at the table and followed the guard to where his mom was waiting. It might take a while to get on her good side again, but he wasn't even guilty this time. Maybe joking around would work. He figured he'd saunter up to her with a "Yo, Catherine! Thanks for springing me!" Sometimes she laughed when he called her by her first name. Hopefully his mom would be chill, and as soon as they got home he could go over to Leah's and see how she was. Maybe take her a sandwich, and tell her how much he cared about her.

All thoughts of Leah and lunch left Josh's mind, however, when he saw his mom's face. Steely-eyed didn't even begin to describe it. If looks could kill, he was burnt toast. Not only was she mad, she seemed to be on a mission. As soon as the guard handed Josh the envelope with his wallet and comm device, she turned on her heel and marched out, saying nothing. Josh hurried behind. No chance he could make her laugh now.

"Mom! What the hell are you mad at me for? I didn't do anything! I'm not lying this time! They had the wrong guy!"

"This time," Josh's mom said through clenched teeth as she stalked through the parking lot, not turning back to look at her son. "THIS time. I'm not waiting for the next time. When will that be?" She got into the car and muttered to herself as she fastened her seat belt. "Next week? Tomorrow? Nope. We're done. We are DONE."

"Hey! Mom!" Josh had to hurry to get in the car before his mom hit the touch screen and sped off.

"Don't talk to me."

"Mom, where are you going? I have to get to Leah's before—"

"I said, don't talk to me. Put your seat belt on and shut up."

Josh shut up. This was weird. Sure, his mom got mad at him all the time, especially when it involved a trip to the jail. But she usually yelled and cried. She didn't act like this; all calm and super mad at the same time. He preferred the old way. And where were they going? He didn't dare ask. No way.

They rode for a while in silence, with Josh sneaking looks at his mom for hints of what was going on, and getting no answers. Then he noticed the location she had entered into the nav system. They were heading for the airport. Were they picking up someone here? When was she gonna talk to him? Yell at him? Anything? The car pulled into a short-term parking lot and lowered into a space. "Come on," Josh's mom ordered as she got out and pulled a backpack and duffel bag from the trunk. Josh followed her into the terminal, and then an airport café. As they sat down, Catherine took an envelope out of her purse and handed it to Josh.

"I said we're done and I meant it. I can't do this anymore, Josh. I can't stand back and watch you ruin your life. Quitting school, getting arrested. You just got off probation, but you're still hanging out with the guys you got in trouble with. You're still breaking into stores. Don't bother lying. I know you are. And no matter what I try to do, it doesn't make any difference. You'll be back in jail sooner rather than later."

She was still angry, but her voice broke. Josh could see how drawn and tired she looked. He tried to shake off the guilt. "Mom, I know. I get it. I'm a loser. But what's going on? Why are we here?" He opened the envelope. "Plane tickets? What for?"

His mom took a deep breath. "You're going to New York. For a month. My sister offered to let you stay with them."

Josh was dumbfounded. "What? No!" No way in hell was what he wanted to say. The guys were counting on him to fence a carful of electronics. And he had to see Leah. She'd think he dumped her for sure if he was gone for a month!

"It's all decided. No arguments. I'm at the end of my rope, Josh. You're going to end up in jail again—for years, probably—unless I do something drastic. Your Uncle Matt and Aunt Ruby agree with me that getting you out of L.A. for a while will be the best thing. Maybe they can help you figure out how to clean up your act. Josh, I'm not trying to punish you. I love you, but I'm scared for you."

"So you're sending me away? To live with some relatives I only met once and don't even remember? Just like that?"

"Your plane leaves in an hour."

"But Mom—"

"I said no arguments," Catherine interrupted. "I'm going to put in more hours at work, since I won't have you to worry about for a while. Hopefully I can catch up on some bills." She tried to sound more cheerful. "Josh, it's been years since you've seen your aunt and uncle, and you were still in diapers the only time you met your cousin Bernie. You're close to the same age, and he's an honor student."

"I have an honor student cousin named Bernie, and I'm gonna spend a month with him? Just kill me now. Seriously. He sounds like a guy who has a collection of argyle sweaters."

Catherine stood up. "You're going. Oh, and give me your comm. When I say you're cut off from L.A., I mean it."

Josh took the comm device off his ear and glumly handed it over. Now there would be no chats with Leah, no messages from the guys, no music on the plane to pass the time.

"Just remember," his mom said. "It's better than jail. Come on; let's get you to the gate."

Josh picked up the bags. He muttered to himself, "Probably not much better," and ran a few steps to catch up with his mom.

"Okay. You're making me do this," he said. "Fine. But will you do one thing for me? Will you call Leah? Please? Tell her where I'm at so she—so she doesn't worry."

"All right. I'll call her when I get home. I promise. And your aunt is going to call me when they have you safe in hand. So no funny business. Your gate's right down there. Get going."

She hugged and kissed him, and before letting him go, whispered in his ear, "Josh, you're not a loser." And with that, she turned and walked away. Josh trudged to his gate, feeling very much like a loser.

The flight was boring. Josh tried to sleep, but couldn't do more than doze off for a few minutes here and there. He kept thinking about his aunt and uncle, and Cousin Bernie of Argyle. Why did they even want him hanging around? They'd probably look down their noses at him, nice respectable people that they were. I suppose everybody hopes some of that respectability will rub off on me, he thought. Josh sighed and closed his eyes. This was going to be one hell of a month.

Opening his eyes, Josh saw other passengers lifting bags out the overhead bins. He must have fallen asleep after all. Hey, I don't know what these people look like, he realized as he made his way out of the plane. Maybe they won't know me either. That fantasy didn't last long, though. Josh's mom must have described him down to his socks, because as soon as he stepped into the terminal, he heard an enthusiastic voice attached to—yes, an argyle vest.

Josh meets his cousin Bernie

"Josh? Is that you? Over here!"

Josh trudged toward his cousin. Damn.

Bernie shook Josh's hand and grabbed his duffel bag. "Is this and the backpack all you've got?"

"Yup, this is it," Josh said.

"Okay! Let's get going, then! We're gonna take the viachute, but I hope you don't mind if we make a stop first. I didn't get my workout in this morning and I hate to skip a day. The gym's on the way home. It's right on the line."

Josh sighed. Bernie didn't seem to notice his lack of enthusiasm. He added, "I've got an extra set of workout clothes in my locker. You can use them if you want to. You're probably tired, but maybe a kilometer or two on the gyrostatic will get you energized."

"Sure, thanks," said Josh. "Maybe." Inwardly, he thought about his most common form of exercise: running from a cop car.

Bernie peppered Josh with questions about his trip till they got to the gym. Josh gave him one-word answers. So what if it was rude? After all, he was tired, right? At the gym, Josh plopped down on a bench, shut his eyes and let Bernie go ahead with his weightlifting. After a while, he looked around and started to wish he had taken Bernie up on the offer to borrow his workout clothes. He was tired, but he also felt restless and on edge. When he felt that way at home, a long walk sometimes helped. Maybe it would've been better to get on a gyrostatic and work off some nervous tension. Oh well. Bernie was done anyway and they could get out of there.

Back on the viachute, Bernie finally got the hint from Josh's lack of response and stopped chattering. It was a pretty silent ride the rest of the way out to Brooklyn. Josh didn't care. He wasn't here to entertain Bernie. He just hoped that his Aunt Ruby and Uncle Matt weren't as incessantly cheerful as his cousin. He held his breath as they went in the front door.

Aunt Ruby met them in the hall. "Hi, Josh! You're just in time for dinner!" she exclaimed, giving Josh a big hug. "Bernie, take Josh's bag down to his room. Do you guys need to wash up? The bathroom's right around the corner, Josh." She called to her husband. "Matt! Our nephew's here! I'll call Catherine and let her know he arrived in one piece." Uncle Matt, coming out of the kitchen, was next to pull Josh into a big bear hug. "Hey, you made it!" he said, then held Josh at arm's length. "Wow, you sure have grown. You're taller than Bernie!"

Like son, like parents, Josh groaned to himself. This cheerfulness bit was just too much. He was sure that after a day or two they'd quit being so friendly and happy. Just an act, that's all it was. His mom must have told them everything. Why would they be glad to see *him*, the criminal of the family?

While they ate dinner, Josh had a chance to check out his new surroundings. The house was neat and clean, homey and comfortable but modern. Aunt Ruby was a pleasant, energetic woman with dark curly hair, dangly earrings, and kind of a hippie vibe. Uncle Matt was a big guy with short hair, jeans and T-shirt. A no-nonsense type. And Josh had guessed right about Bernie. Red hair and glasses. Preppy to the hilt, from his argyle vest and polo shirt right down to his chinos and loafers.

The food was good; baked spaghetti, fresh bread and salad. Josh ate more than he thought he would. And everyone laughed, even Josh, when Uncle Matt accidentally belched and then apologized for it by saying, "My compliments to the chef!"

Watching Bernie and his parents, Josh felt a bit of envy, in spite of himself. Make fun of it all you wanted, but here was a real family. You could tell they respected and cared about each other. Josh hardly ever talked to his mom, much less sat down for a meal with her. His dad had split when Josh was three years old and his mom had been on her own ever since. A twinge of guilt replaced the envy in his mind. On her own. With a delinquent loser son to add to her trouble.

He looked at his aunt again. The two sisters, Ruby and his mom Catherine, had grown up together, but were so far apart now. He could see some resemblance. They were both attractive and tall, with dark hair and dark eyes, but Ruby was healthy, happy and vibrant. Bernie had told him she was a fifth grade teacher. It would take a lot of energy to do that job! Josh pictured his mom: tired, sad and beaten down. She worked two jobs, just trying to make ends meet. Josh couldn't push aside the thought that he was to blame for her rough life. Maybe it wasn't all his fault, but he sure hadn't done anything to help.

"Ready for lemon pie, everybody?" asked his aunt, startling Josh out of his thoughts. "I had a load of papers to grade today, so it's fresh from the replicator, not one of my handmade ones."

"You spoil us anyway, Ruby," said Uncle Matt. "On my next day off, I'll whip up my famous chocolate cookies."

"And I'll make a pie this weekend," countered Aunt Ruby. "Then Josh can judge who the best baker is: you, me, or the replicator!"

"Sounds good," said Josh as he accepted a piece of pie. He couldn't help smiling a little. After dessert, Bernie jumped up. "Mom, I'm gonna show Josh his room. Then I'll come up and do the dishes, okay?"

"Okay," said his mom. "Take your time."

Josh stood up to follow his cousin. "Um, thanks for dinner," he offered.

"No special thanks necessary," said Uncle Matt. "You're family, Josh."

Josh followed Bernie down the stairs. It looked like he was going to be sleeping in the den or family room. The room had an easy chair, a desk, a pull-out couch that was already made up into a bed, and several boxes. Not cardboard boxes, but good-sized wooden boxes, like chests or something. They all had different shapes and designs.

"Here you go," said Bernie. "I know it's not like your own bedroom exactly, but we'll try to give you as much privacy as you need. Anything you want right now?"

"Nah," said Josh. "I mean no thanks. I'm pretty tired. Guess I'll go to bed."

"Sure. No problem," said Bernie. "You know, Josh, I'm really glad you're here. I've sort of felt bad having a cousin all the way across the country who I didn't even know. This will be cool."

"Yeah," said Josh. "Absolutely. Good night, Bernie."

Josh took a deep breath after Bernie had left. How was he going to stand it here for a month? He tried not to think about Leah. Hopefully his mom had remembered to talk to her. Who knows what good it did, though? Leah probably hated him right now.

Josh glanced around the room. There were five different chests. Some were arranged on shelves that must have been custom made for them. A few were on the floor, and one was next to the easy chair. The chair looked pretty comfy. He plopped down in it and looked at the chest. It was a simple design: polished black wood with silver metal trim. It had a lock, but out of curiosity, Josh tried the lid. It opened. Huh, he thought. These people are too trusting.

The chest was full of stuff. Josh dug around and picked up a strange looking device. It was about the size of his hand and looked like one of those things they used to call a cell phone. It was pink. He pushed a few buttons, but of course it didn't work. He lifted a divider out of the chest and dug deeper. There were old tickets for theater productions in New York City. One of them was stamped with the date *December 6, 2005*. Wow. That was almost one hundred years ago. Who did this stuff belong to? Why was it here?

Josh started thinking about the person who had owned these things so long ago. Who was it? Why were these things important to them? All of a sudden he felt funny for looking in the chest.

He hadn't asked permission. It felt even weirder to think that his family trusted him to sleep in this room without stealing anything from all these chests. Josh closed the lid on the chest—and on the thought of lifting something from it. Maybe he could sleep now. He climbed into bed and sure enough, he was out like a light.

When Josh woke up it was to the sound of Bernie's dad calling his name. "Josh! Sleepyhead! You're coming to work with me, big guy! The upstairs bathroom is free, and breakfast is almost ready." Josh figured there was no way out of it, so he took a quick shower, dressed, and made his way to the kitchen. In the middle of a mouthful of scrambled eggs, Bernie's dad announced "Oh, by the way, I'm a cop. You'll be riding along with me today." Josh almost choked. Did he say cop? Like police officer? Seriously? Gee, thanks, Mom. You really do have it in for me. No wonder you took my comm. I can't talk to you, I can't talk to Leah. I can't reach the guys. I can't even play any music to drown out the sounds of Happyland. And you've got me hanging out with an NYPD cop.

In the car with his uncle, Josh stared straight ahead, thinking. How much had his mom told Uncle Matt about the trouble Josh had been in? The times he had been in jail and on probation? Was this supposed to be some kind of tough love? Was Uncle Matt going to start yelling at him about getting his act together? Or worse yet, was he going to take him to the station and dump him in jail, for some kind of "scared straight" thing? Was that the plan all along? Josh would never forgive his mom.

They walked into the station together. Josh was apprehensive and quiet, but Uncle Matt was smiling and upbeat. He introduced Josh all around, acting like he was proud to have him as a nephew. A few times, someone asked Josh if he was in college yet or what his career plans were. Josh didn't know what to say. He was ashamed and embarrassed. Most people his age had goals, plans, things to look forward to. Josh had none of that. He hadn't planned to be living the life of a petty criminal. His mom sure hadn't dreamed of this as a career for him, and he knew Leah wasn't proud of having a crook and a dropout for a boyfriend. He was beginning to see how much he had let them down, and himself too.

Josh relaxed a little as they headed to his uncle's vehicle and he realized he wasn't going to get tossed in a cell. They spent the day patrolling and responding to calls. Josh watched as his uncle handled every situation with confidence and strength. He showed respect and kindness to everyone, even the criminals. Criminals like Josh. Even when people were belligerent, he kept his cool and listened to them. You could see the faith in humanity shining through his eyes as he did the best he could with every situation.

Josh had never seen a police officer act like this before. He was astounded. By the time the day was over and they were back at the station, he felt proud to be introduced as Matt's nephew to the officers coming on for the next shift.

They met Bernie at the gym on the way home, and this time Josh borrowed some clothes and hopped on a gyrostatic. He was surprised that the workout didn't make him tired. He felt more awake than he had in a long time. It pumped him up.

Dinner and conversation were a little easier that night. Maybe they weren't faking. Maybe his family honestly liked him. Maybe he'd make it through the month after all.

Josh rode with his uncle the rest of the week, and they developed a pleasant routine: breakfast after Bernie and Aunt Ruby left for school, chatting in the car on the way to the station, Josh watching Uncle Matt fulfill his duties as one of New York's finest, working out at the gym—sometimes with Bernie or Aunt Ruby—and home to supper and an evening with the family.

Josh slept well, too, and was surprised at the amount of energy he had. It was rough getting up early the first few mornings, with Bernie or Uncle Matt yelling down the stairs, "Come on, Josh! Get vertical!" But after those first few pushes to get out of bed, get moving and join the world, Josh started to feel so much more ready each morning. He even got his uncle to do a couple of early workouts before his shift started!

As much as Josh was starting to enjoy his time in New York, he still worried about Leah, his gang and that latest batch of stolen goods. He wondered how his mom was doing. It wasn't so bad here after all, but he felt as if he was just marking time until L.A. and all his problems would be in his face again, with no solutions.

A few evenings later, Josh had officially declared Aunt Ruby's strawberry pie the winner—by a nose—over Uncle Matt's chocolate cookies, with the replicator coming in a distant third. After promising to referee a rematch, he and Bernie wandered downstairs to Josh's room. Josh threw himself into the easy chair before his cousin could get to it.

Bernie plopped down on the sofa bed. "Josh, can I talk to you?" he began.

"Sure. Something wrong?" Josh asked.

"No. I just don't know how to start without sounding like a dweeb." Bernie hesitated.

"But you are a dweeb. Thought you knew that by now." Josh reached over to punch his cousin in the shoulder and they both laughed.

"Ow. But listen, Josh. I know you've been having sort of a bad run. Believe it or not, I've had some rough patches myself. And I've been on a few ride-alongs with my dad, too. It really opened my eyes to see what he goes through every day."

"He's a great guy, Bernie," Josh agreed.

"Yeah. But I still didn't get it. His drive and determination, I mean, and my mom's, too. When I started high school I didn't care about studying, or taking care of myself, or planning for the future. Mom and Dad would lecture me but what they said didn't stick. Then they opened the chests."

"Huh? These boxes?"

"Josh, when my mom and dad dragged me down here and taught me what these chests mean, I didn't need lectures anymore. I didn't need any more pushing to do my schoolwork or get out of bed to go to the gym. Don't get me wrong. I'm not perfect. But it all made sense after that day."

"That's a lot for a box to do, Bernie." Josh grinned, but he was only half joking. He wanted to hear more.

"They're called life chests. Way more than a box." Bernie took his turn punching Josh's shoulder. "My mom became the life chest keeper for our family when I was sixteen. They go back four generations. Haven't you looked in any of them?"

"No. Well, just this one, a little. I wasn't sure—"

"Let's start with that one, then," Bernie interrupted. "They're meant to be looked at and shared, Josh. That's the whole point."

Bernie moved to the floor and opened the polished black chest that Josh had looked at his first night in New York. He took things out of the chest as he told Josh about its owner. This life chest, called the Havana, was their great-grandmother's. Her name was Ashley Yost. They saw old-fashioned 2D photos of her as a tall, pretty girl who apparently was a good basketball player. She had hairdressing things, and an old doll called Barbie. It looked like she had given Barbie a rough haircut or two.

They found some round discs that Bernie called DVDs. Josh had never seen these before, but Bernie had a device that could play them. One DVD showed Ashley speaking in front of a camera, talking about the news. This must've been what she had studied, because they also found a diploma for a broadcasting school. The boys laughed as they looked back at Barbie and agreed that Great-Grandma Ashley was a better newscaster than a beautician. Other pictures and articles showed that she was a businessperson, too. At one point in her career she managed a furniture store called Urban Barn.

Josh started to see why someone would want to keep memories in a chest like this. You could look back on your life choices and accomplishments with pride, and your family would be inspired by them too. Well, that would be great for some people, he thought. I've got nothing to make anybody proud. Josh sighed and turned away from the chest, but Bernie's enthusiasm soon brought him out of his self-pity session.

"Wasn't Great-Grandma Ashley cool?" said Bernie as he closed the Havana chest. "Look over here. This one with the leather straps on it is her son's. He's our Grandpa Noah."

"Does his chest have a name, too?" asked Josh.

"Yeah. They all do. His is called the New Yorker," answered Bernie, opening the lid of the honey colored maple wood chest.

As the evening wore on, Bernie showed Josh amazing things from Grandpa Noah's life chest and from his mom's. There were keepsakes and trinkets, diplomas, letters, journals with stories and poems, jewelry, watches, coins from around the world, 3D photosims and the old fashioned 2D photos. And every single thing he picked up had a memory attached to it. Bernie was able to tell Josh about people neither of them had ever met, because the things they saved in their life chests kept their stories alive. Josh started to see where his family came from and what they were made of. He even saw where Bernie got his red hair—their Grandpa Noah was a big, burly red-headed guy. He collected everything about beer!

After they had finished looking at the three chests, something occurred to Josh. "Do you have a life chest?" he asked his cousin.

"Oh, yeah. But there's nothing special in mine like in these older ones. You can look at it if you want." Bernie opened the lid of a chest that looked like it belonged on a pirate ship. "I have some school awards, and recordings of piano recitals." He seemed embarrassed. "Dumb stuff, I guess."

"No, it's cool. I bet it's called the Pirate chest, right?" It would be so easy to make fun of Bernie. He was the kind of guy Josh and his friends back home laughed at all the time. Hell, they would even beat them up now and then. But right now Josh felt like he would pound anybody who tried to harass his cousin. "You should be proud of yourself."

Bernie smiled. "Thanks, Josh. I got my life chest when I was little and was really into pirates." He looked around the room. "Hey, there's one chest left. That one over there with the map design on it. I saved it for last because I think it's the best one. It belonged to our great-great-grandfather. His name was Kim Yost. It's getting late, though, so do you mind if I head upstairs to bed? I have an exam tomorrow. Go ahead and look at it on your own."

"Okay," Josh answered. "Thanks for showing me the life chests."

"Do you see what I mean about these chests? Seeing and touching our family's history—the first time I saw them it really got me thinking. And the things I learned from this last one here—well, it changed everything for me. I think it might change things for you too." Both boys stood up, and Josh started the bear hug this time.

"It might sound hokey, but you've got what it takes to have a great life, Josh. And it's up to you if you have that life or not," said Bernie as he started up the stairs.

Josh thought for a moment. Hokey? Maybe. But true? Maybe. He turned back to Great-Great-Grandpa Kim's life chest. It was a rustic, leather-strapped, battered old chest sitting on the floor near the desk. Josh pulled the desk chair over to it, sat down, and looked closer. With the map design on top, nail heads all around, and the leather straps, it looked like a chest that had been around. If this one has a name, it's got to be the Traveler, Josh thought. He began to explore its contents. There was a lot to explore!

A few hours passed with Josh barely noticing the time. Finally, he stood up to take a break. He yawned, stretched, and threw himself onto the bed. So many images filled his mind! Bernie really had saved the best for last. One of the first things he had found in the chest was a moon rock. His Great-Great-Grandpa Kim had a little box with a piece of black rock in it that was actually from the moon! Josh had to ask Bernie how Gramps had gotten it. He also found a lot of old car photos in the chest. Really cool vehicles, all black, and they looked pretty racy for an old guy to be driving. Josh thought about what it would feel like to drive one of those old-style cars, gripping the road and squealing around. A lot different than the levicars everybody drove now. And probably more fun.

There were stacks of other photos in the chest, from all around the world, and keepsakes from these different places, too. He collected paper money and coins from everywhere he had been. Josh looked at several passports, all stamped full. They were like travel journals in themselves. Great-Great-Grandpa Kim had been an adventurer, that's for sure! But there were also business cards, company reports, and letters from people he worked with. He didn't just play. He worked hard. He seemed like the type of person who put his all into everything he did; who really lived his life to the fullest. As he got up from the bed to dig further into the chest, Josh wondered aloud, "How did you do it, Gramps?"

The answer to his question came with the next thing Josh picked up from the bottom of the life chest: a book. Not a tablet or ebook, but an actual book with pages. You never saw those anymore. And it wasn't just any old book. It was a book that Great-Great-Grandpa Kim had written! The title was *Pumptitude: Pump Up Your Attitude and Gain Altitude: 68 Ways to Make a Great Life*. Josh couldn't wait to read it. He wanted to know more about this ancestor of his and his philosophy of life. He opened the old book carefully and began to read. And read, and read.

The next morning, Bernie told his folks about going through the life chests with Josh. Instead of calling him for breakfast, Matt peeked downstairs to see Josh asleep with the copy of *Pumptitude* next to him on the bed. "The kid can sleep in today, I guess," he chuckled.

Josh discovers the life chests

During his last week in New York, Josh and his family spent some time exploring the city. After discovering the life chests and reading *Pumptitude*, Josh felt like he had been given new eyes, a new heart, and a beginner's mind. He tried to remember everything he did and saw. He bought keepsakes. He shook hands with people he didn't know and tried to make eye contact with everyone he could. He asked questions and listened. He told the truth about himself. He was starting to think he had a life worth living and a future worth building. He started to appreciate his family—and the whole idea of family—like he never had before. He didn't want to let them down. He didn't want to let himself down. The past was the past, and he couldn't change it. What he *could* do was forgive himself, learn from his mistakes, and take charge of his own destiny.

Josh thought about his past, and what his future might be. He remembered reading in *Pumptitude* about the Japanese principle of kaizen, meaning continuous improvement. From this moment on, his life was either going to get worse or get better. If he wanted better, he was going to have to work, and work hard, for that Constant and Never-ending Improvement,

35

or CANI, as his great-great-grandfather called it. Josh made a promise to himself. Kaizen it would be.

It was hard to say goodbye when the day came for Josh to go back to Los Angeles. Uncle Matt, Aunt Ruby and Bernie really were family now, and there were lots of hugs and promises to stay in touch. Josh had not only survived the month, but thanks to what he had learned from his family, the life chests, and Gramps' book, he was on his way to making a whole new life. He felt ready for the challenges and opportunities that he would face back home.

While Josh was finishing up his packing, Bernie came downstairs to the family room. "I know how much you liked going through Great-Great-Grandpa Kim's life chest," he said. "But I haven't had a chance to look at it with you. Got a couple minutes?"

"Sure," said Josh, tossing a t-shirt in his duffel bag and plopping down on the floor. Bernie opened the chest. "What was your favorite thing in here?"

"The *Pumptitude* book, for sure. But besides that, I really liked the way he wrote down his thoughts. Kind of like a combination journal and map."

"Pretty cool, huh?" Bernie picked up a drawing. "Some people call them mind maps. This is the one he drew back in 1983 when he came up with the idea of building life chests."

"That was his idea? Sweet."

"Yeah. He got the idea from an ancient Chinese tradition. I wish we would've had the time to read the journal from his first trip to Asia in1983, but it's pretty long. That's where the story is," explained Bernie.

"I hope I get a chance to read it someday," said Josh as he picked up another old map. It was made of leather, rolled up and tied with a leather cord. "This map is really cool. I've never seen anything like it. Do you know what it is?"

Bernie took the map, untied the cord and unrolled it. He smoothed out the curled edges and thought for a minute. "Great-Great-Grandpa Kim got this map on that same trip, the first time he was in Asia. He was in Bangkok, Thailand, I think. The man who gave it to him said it was a treasure map."

"Cool," said Josh. "What was the treasure? Jewels or something?"

"Gold, I think," answered Bernie. "Gramps wrote in his journal that there was a legend in the man's family, handed down for several generations. The legend says there's gold buried inside the Great Wall of China. This map is supposed to describe the treasure and show where it is."

"Wow," said Josh. "Wish I knew how to read Chinese. I sure could use some treasure!"

"You and me both, cousin," agreed Bernie. "I'd love to learn more about the story behind that map. But it'll have to wait till our next visit. I better let you finish packing."

After gathering his things and eating a farewell slice of Ruby's award-winning strawberry pie, Josh was ready to go to the airport. Ruby and Matt headed out to the car. Josh was about to follow when Bernie pulled him aside. He seemed to be ready to bust out of his argyle sweater—and not from too much pie.

"Josh, wait a minute. Here's a copy of *Pumptitude* for you to keep."

"My own copy! That's great. Thanks a lot, Bernie," said Josh. "I want to read it again for sure."

Bernie had more to say. "Hang on. There's something else I have to tell you. Something really incredible. Josh, Great-Great-Grandpa Kim wrote another book."

"Besides *Pumptitude*? Cool. Do you have it?"

"Yup, and you have a copy now too. Mom said it was okay to give it to you. It's called *Maximum Pumptitude* and it's in your bag; but promise you won't read it until you get home."

"Okay. But why?"

"I really can't explain it. Just trust me. As soon as you get home tonight, sit down with your mom and read Appendix A. Josh, it'll blow your mind! Read that part and then call me, okay? I'll be waiting to hear from you."

"Sure. But can't you tell me what it's about?"

"Nope. Your mom has to read it with you. Then you'll understand. Josh, our families' life chests are pretty amazing, right? I mean, the treasures in them and the stories they tell? Well, this is the most amazing story of them all. It's almost like the life chest gives the stories a special power."

The look on Josh's face was a mixture of amusement and puzzlement. Bernie laughed.

"Okay, okay. I know it sounds crazy. Just call me as soon as you read Appendix A! Come on, my folks are waiting."

A few hours later, Josh settled into his seat on the plane. He thought of his mom and smiled to himself. Now he realized what she had been hoping for when she packed him off to New York and cut off his communication. She knew what he was going to find in those chests, because she had seen them too. She had grown up with them. What bothered him, though, was that his mom had not been using the life chest lessons in her own life, much less passing them on to him. She didn't even have a life chest of her own. That would change soon, Josh thought, and his smile returned.

This flight was a lot different from his trip a month ago. It wasn't boring, because Josh had a lot to think about. He felt like a different person—stronger, happier, and healthier—but there were things from his past he knew he had to face and a lot he had to change. He was worried about being able to stand up to the guys and tell them he was through with stealing and fencing. He was anxious about getting his high school diploma and finding a job. He was really worried about Leah—how she was doing and if she wanted to still be with him. But now he was armed with a plan. He had a copy of *Pumptitude* and it would be his guide. He had a new perspective on things after looking through the life chests with Bernie and learning the stories of his family. Those stories revealed time after time that nobody was immune to setbacks and failures, but the people who could forgive their failures and move on could do amazing things. They weren't stuck in a "this or that" mindset. Gramps had quoted another great thinker named Jim Collins in *Pumptitude*. His idea was to embrace the genius of the AND rather than the tyranny of the OR.

Josh thought about the genius of the AND as he looked out the window. The plane flew over banks of blindingly white clouds. They were clean and new, not gray and gritty like the ones down at city level in L.A. Josh wanted a clean slate like that. Sure, he'd still make mistakes. But he knew that he could set high standards for himself AND recover from mistakes. He could make plans AND allow for those plans to change if need be. In the past, Josh thought that he had to work hard at school OR have fun. It had to be one or the other. Of course I chose fun and quit school, he thought bitterly to himself.

But it was clean slate time. Forgive your failures and move on, right? Right! He was going to work hard to finish school AND have fun. He would try to improve his own outlook on life AND work on his relationships with Leah and his mom.

Josh looked out the window again and saw the plane start to break the line of clouds and descend. Here we go, he thought. I don't have to choose between "this OR that." I can embrace the genius of the AND.

Then Josh remembered that he had Gramps' second book, too: *Maximum Pumptitude*. Bernie had told him to read Appendix A with his mom as soon as he got home. His cousin wouldn't give away any more, except that it was something incredible. He even hinted that it was almost magical. Well, anything's possible, thought Josh. And he surprised himself. He actually believed it. My life CAN be great, he assured himself. And if I really want a great life, it's gonna be up to me.

After landing in L.A., Josh waited in the baggage area, straining to spot his treasures as they dropped onto the belt. There they were, the best part of everything he brought back: two life chests. He smiled when he saw them, and grabbed them off the belt as quick as he could. Aunt Ruby and Uncle Matt were so generous. They insisted on buying a life chest for him and one for his mom. It had been exciting to go online and pick out the chests. He hoped his mom liked hers. It was the Salzburg, the same style as Aunt Ruby's: real pretty but not fussy. Just like Mom, Josh thought with satisfaction.

With his luggage cart stacked high, Josh headed to where his mom would be waiting for him. He was happy. Happy to be home, happy to have spent the past month learning about what could change his future, and happy to see his mom. She really was always there for him, and now Josh understood what that meant.

Catherine had a nervous look on her face as her son came into view, but it turned to relief as Josh ran to meet her with a big smile. Then he gave her a hug and kiss, and the relief became amazement. The sullen, reticent boy she had said goodbye to a month ago had become a new man.

Josh and his mom reunite

Ruby had called that morning to share some of the details, but nothing could have prepared her for the joy she felt in seeing how Josh had changed. He seemed healthy and looked confident. She could swear he even looked a few inches taller!

Catherine was all smiles on the drive home. She wanted to hear about the trip, but Josh was worried about Leah.

"Did you call her, Mom?" he asked anxiously.

"Yes, and I went to see her too, Josh. I wanted to make sure Leah and her parents understood that you didn't abandon her. I told them that you were away for a while to try to get your life together, but you still loved her."

"And? What did Leah say?"

"She wants you to call her as soon as you get home."

Josh leaned back in his seat, relieved. "Thanks for laying the groundwork, Mom," he said. "I know it's up to me now to make things right with Leah. I'll call her when we get home and go see her first thing in the morning. I've really missed her."

Josh spent the rest of the trip telling his mom some of the highlights of his time in New York. Most importantly, he told her about seeing the life chests in his aunt and uncle's home. He explained some of the lessons he had learned and the inspiration he had gotten from exploring the treasures that the life chests contained.

"Mom, things will be different now. I really believe it," Josh said confidently. "I'm going to make a life worth living and I'm going to do my best to make your life easier, too. Someday I'll buy you a new car, and your own house! And you know what? Uncle Matt and Aunt Ruby gave us our own life chests! That's what those two big cartons are."

Josh's enthusiasm was infectious. His mom's face brightened as she listened. She promised that she would begin to fill her new life chest. "Let's start this new phase of our lives together, Josh," she said with a smile. "I know there are a lot of positive changes I can make, too."

When they got home, Catherine gave Josh his comm device. He called Leah, still a little nervous about the state of their relationship. He told her that he had missed her, and couldn't wait to see her in the morning. He was relieved and happy to hear that she had missed him too.

"We have a lot to talk about," he said. "This trip was life-changing, Leah. I really see the world differently now. I'm finally excited about my future, and I want you to be in it. If you want to be."

"You almost sound like a different person. Is this really my boyfriend?" teased Leah. They both laughed. "I can't wait to hear about everything," she said. "I'll see you tomorrow, Babe."

After they signed off, Josh unpacked the life chests and proudly carried his mom's into her bedroom. He placed the plane tickets from his trip into her life chest. He had also written his mom a long note, trying to express everything he had learned while he was gone. He asked his mom to forgive him for making her life so rough and not appreciating her. He put the note next to the tickets and closed the lid. That note would be the beginning of a new understanding between them.

Josh then took his own life chest, a Pirate chest like Bernie's, to his bedroom. It seemed like years since he had been in that room. The clutter and mess looked like it belonged to somebody else. He dove in and started cleaning. His living space needed to be worthy of him and his new life chest.

Josh's mom looked in and smiled to see Josh making his bed. "I thought we'd go out to eat tonight to celebrate," she said, leaning against the door frame. "Are you hungry?"

"I sure am," said Josh. "But Mom, there's something we have to do before we go. Did you know that my great-great-grandpa Kim Yost wrote books? I have two of them."

"Yeah, I guess so," answered his mom. "I always liked to look at the pictures in his life chest but I wasn't much interested in the books. I think Ruby read them, though."

"His first book is called *Pumptitude*, and it's great. I read it in New York, and I got a copy, so you can read it next. But here's the other one." Digging in his bag, Josh pulled out a brown paper parcel. He carefully opened it to reveal the copy of *Maximum Pumptitude* that Bernie had stowed under his socks.

"Wow! That sure is an antique!" his mom said.

"I know. Aunt Ruby is trusting me with it and I'll keep it safe. But here's the thing, Mom. I promised Bernie we'd read part of it as soon as I got home." He paged through the book. "Here it is. Appendix A. Sit down, Mom."

"Right now?"

"Yeah. Bernie said it was incredible, and we had to read it together. He wants me to call him after."

"Okay. I can't imagine what it is, but it sounds important." Catherine sat on the bed next to her son. "Do you want to read it out loud?"

Josh began to read *Maximum Pumptitude Appendix A: The Life Chest Story*. Bernie had been right. There was no way he could have explained it. Josh and his mom couldn't explain it, either. Josh read it, out loud, without comment from either one of them, but the amazement showed on their faces and in Josh's voice as he read.

What he read was this: a short story, written back in 2013, about two cousins, well into the future. One in New York, a typical "good kid", and one in Los Angeles, a guy in a lot of trouble. They met when the L.A. kid was shipped off to New York for a month. He decided to turn his life around after learning the stories of his family's life chests and reading his great-great-grandfather's books. The two families were similar to Josh and Bernie's. Everything in the story was similar to what Josh and Bernie had been through. In fact, the cousins' names were *Josh* and *Bernie*!

Catherine and Josh were both speechless. After Josh closed the book, he set his comm device to share mode and called Bernie. His cousin picked up on the first buzz.

"Josh! What did you think?" said Bernie excitedly. "Aunt Catherine! Isn't it amazing?"

"I don't get it, Bernie! It's us. The story is about us!" Josh was at a loss for words after that. "How…who…?"

His cousin laughed. "Well, if you ever wondered how I got the name Bernie, now you know. My mom read that story when she was a girl. She decided back then if she ever had a son, he was going to be saddled—I mean blessed—with that name."

Josh's mom burst out, "But I never read the book! I just liked the name Josh! I don't know why; I never even knew anyone named Josh!"

"We wondered about that when Josh was born, Catherine." Ruby had joined in the call too. "I didn't think you had read the books. But you and I—we weren't close then, so I didn't—"

"I know, Ruby," answered her sister. "It's okay. I was pushing everyone away back then. But this story is about our sons, written before they were born! And I named my baby Josh! Even if it's just a coincidence, I can't believe it!"

"To tell you the truth, I had forgotten about it for years," said Ruby. "Then you and I started talking again, and the boys got older, and Josh—well, his troubles started. I didn't know what to do to help. Then I remembered the book. I got it out of our great-grandpa Kim's life chest, and when I read it again, I was stunned. I knew Josh had to come here."

Everyone was quiet for a minute, thinking about the events and changes of the past month, all predicted by a story written eighty-eight years earlier.

Uncle Matt was on the line too. He broke the silence. "It's amazing," he said. "I can't explain it either, but it's truly amazing."

"None of us can explain it," said Bernie. "I guess it's one of those mysteries that you have to accept. A life chest mystery. That book sat in Great-Great-Grandpa's life chest for so many years. I'm inclined to think it took on sort of a life of its own. I'm actually developing a theory, see, about the power of intention and putting objects or writings into a life chest." Bernie's voice changed from studious to animated. "I wrote a description of my ideal girl. I put it in my life chest, and so in a couple years I expect to meet her. I hope so, anyway."

Bernie's parents laughed, but Josh said, "Go for it! Anything's possible! Just make sure one of the requirements is that she likes argyle sweaters."

"It's a mystery, all right," Josh's mom shook her head. "I guess these life chests really are something special. Thanks, Ruby, Matt, and you too, Bernie. For everything."

At the restaurant later that evening, the conversation between Josh and his mom was very different than the one they had a month earlier in the airport café. Mother and son talked, laughed, cried a little, and felt closer than they had in years. As amazing as it was to find himself in a book written before he was born, Josh knew his journey to a great life was just beginning, and it wouldn't be easy. He expressed his fears about making the changes in his life that he wanted so much. His mom reminded him to apply the lessons he'd learned in *Pumptitude* and assured him that she'd be there for him. They promised to support each other.

Josh went to bed that night smiling. He was armed and dangerous. He chuckled to himself. A month ago, that would have meant something very bad. Tonight it meant: Look out, world! I'm going to make a great life for myself. I'm worth it. I'm worth the time and energy and learning that it's going to take. I'm proud of my family and I'm going to make them proud of me. I'll fill my life chest with amazing achievements so future generations can understand what got them where they are. Hey, maybe I'll get a CANI tattoo. Thanks, Great-Great-Grandpa, for inspiring me to adopt a life of "Constant and Never-ending Improvement!"

Fifty years. Wow. Relishing the memories, Josh smiled and pulled up his sleeve. His mom had protested when he went to the tattoo parlor, but the CANI design on his right arm had been a good reminder of his commitment to making a great life. He couldn't talk Bernie into getting one. It didn't go with his "look". I'll call him right now, Josh thought, and tease him about his argyle sweaters. But before he could say "Bernie" into his comm device, the door slid open and April stomped in.

"Is the party over? What's the matter, Blossom?" he asked.

"Grandpa!" April was angry, and near tears. "My friend Michael says all your stories are fake! I told him about you and Grandma flying in the old-fashioned airplane you built, and he didn't believe it. He said you should just admit that you make up all the stories you tell me. But they really happened, didn't they?"

Josh thought of another ancient book that had been in Great-Great-Grandpa Kim's life chest: Marco Polo's book of stories about his adventures. Bernie sent it as a birthday gift soon after Josh had gotten back to L.A. He chuckled. "Blossom, they said the same thing to Marco Polo. And I've got the same answer. You kids haven't heard *half* the stories I've got. Tell Michael that!"

"Okay, Grandpa!" April was all smiles again as she walked out of the room, but she turned back at the door, puzzled. "Grandpa, who's Marco Polo?"

Josh chuckled and waved her away. "Another time, Blossom, another time!"

THE ORIGINAL

Life Chest

Part One

The History of the Dynasty Chest

— Chapter 1 —

Marco Polo and His Guide:

The Dynasty Chest is Created

In November, a few months after the birthday party, April spent the mid-semester school break at Josh and Leah's while her parents went on an anniversary cruise.

"Grandpa, I'm bored. My homework's all done and it's raining," complained April, wandering into Josh's study on the third evening. "Grandma told me to come see you. She's bored with me saying I'm bored."

"I can imagine," said Josh. "Just a minute, Blossom." He finished dusting a picture frame, set it back on its shelf and crouched down to his granddaughter's level. "Don't you like it at Grandpa and Grandma's anymore?" he asked with an exaggerated pout.

"Yes, I like it here. Don't make that face, Grandpa!" April laughed and tried to push Josh's mouth up into a smile.

"Okay, okay! That tickles!" laughed Josh. "So what's wrong, then?"

"You know what's wrong. I wanted to go with Mom and Dad on their trip. It'll be forever till they're back."

"Forever? That's a pretty long time."

"Oh, Grandpa. I know it's just a week. But it feels like it's gonna be forever. What if they forget about me and don't come back at all?"

"They won't do that. They miss you, too, Blossom."

"OK. I guess I can wait a while longer," said April.

Josh stood up. "You know, that reminds me of a story. Can you help me find something in my life chest?"

"Sure! What are we looking for?" April climbed into Josh's old leather easy chair and eagerly opened the lid of the life chest sitting next to it. She loved looking at the treasures and hearing her grandpa's stories about them.

"One of my books about Marco Polo. You asked me who he was at your birthday party, remember?"

"Those old-fashioned books with real pages? You have a lot of them. Is this it, Grandpa?"

"Yeah, that's it. Blossom, your parents will be home in less than a week. Marco Polo waited for his father for fifteen years. And get this! He wasn't sure his dad even knew that he existed!"

"Really? Why didn't his father know he existed, Grandpa? Why was he gone for so long?"

"You want to hear the story?"

"Yes!"

"Okay, get comfortable." April handed the book to Josh and sat on a floor pillow. Josh settled into his reclining chair. "The story starts in Italy, way back in 1269. Did I tell you Marco was fifteen years old?"

"Uh-huh. So he was a teenager. Did he have a girlfriend?"

"Nope. Just listen, Blossom." Josh opened the book and began to read the story.

Every day since he could remember, young Marco did the same thing. After the evening meal he wandered down to the harbor. Sound carried over the waves. He could hear music, laughing, children crying, and over it all the sound of the water. The sounds of Venice, his home. He stared as far as he could out to sea, watching the sun set and wondering if he would see his father's ship come over the horizon. How would he know it even if he did see it? He would know. He was sure of it.

Now and again he would hear people in the town whisper about his father and uncle. They would shake their heads and click their tongues in sympathy for him, the boy whose mother was dead and whose father had been gone since before he was born. The whispers were full of pity. When he mentioned the talk to his aunt, she hugged him and told him not to listen.

Marco's mother's sister, her husband, and other relatives were the only family he knew. His aunt loved him as one of her own. She fed him, clothed him, and taught him his childhood lessons. He was fifteen years old now, and for the last few years his uncle had taken over his education. Marco would become a traveling merchant, like his father and the other men in his family. He learned mathematics, foreign currency, appraising, and the details of cargo shipping.

But what of his father, Niccolò? Marco's mother had been pregnant when his father left on a trading mission to Asia with his brother Maffeo. She had died when Marco was a baby. But his father was out there, somewhere, and he was as much a mystery to Marco as his mother was a ghost.

Sitting on the shore night after night, Marco wondered what life would have in store for him. Something was going to happen, and it was out there where his father was. He just had to wait for it. He would be ready. He would know his father's ship when it came in and it would be his ship as well.

The brothers told incredible stories of their time in the East. They had met the great Kublai Khan, and the Khan had requested that the brothers return with oil from the holy lamp of Jerusalem, as well as with messages from the Pope. Niccolò and Matteo planned the return trip while they waited for a new Pope to be appointed. Marco was excited to join his father and uncle on the journey, and he didn't have to beg to convince his father to take him along. Niccolò was pleased with his son's intelligence, knowledge and eagerness to learn. He was happy to have Marco join him in the adventurer's life, and Marco was thrilled. This was what he had been hoping for all those evenings, searching the horizon for the ship that would carry his father to him.

In 1271, when all that they needed had been acquired, the three started out on what would become their longest journey. Niccolò enjoyed seeing his son's reactions to the sights and sounds along the way. They traveled by ship, on horseback and by camel, through rough seas, barren deserts and treacherous mountains toward the mysterious East.

Marco, now seventeen years old, drank in every experience, even the hardships of extreme weather, hunger and thirst. He tried to remember everything that happened. In fact, he couldn't sleep at night with all the sights and sounds swirling through his head. He decided to keep a daily journal, because once he had written down at least a few notes about what he experienced during the day, he was able to quiet his mind enough to rest at night.

Finally, after three years of traveling, the trio arrived in Dadu, the site of Kublai Khan's Imperial Palace, in 1274. Marco was twenty years old. Niccolò and Maffeo received an audience with Kublai Khan, who had been waiting for their return. The Khan had a great interest in how Europeans lived, and was eager to hear about Italian society and Western religion. The brothers were offered positions in the Khan's government, and were happy to settle down and stop traveling, at least for a while. But Marco had just gotten started.

The Great Kublai Khan

"You have my blessing to continue exploring," Niccolò assured Marco. "And don't forget, my son. Abundance will come to you when you have the desire to accept it. Believe that good things will happen, and they will." He clapped his son on the shoulder.

"Now you must hire your own guide," Niccolò said to Marco. "Your guide will be your closest companion. A good one will not be merely a servant. He will be like a brother, and even a protector. A bad one will endanger your life."

The three Italians made their way to the marketplace where men waited to be hired for various jobs. More and more European explorers had begun to travel around Asia, and some of the locals hired themselves out as guides. Marco felt nervous and self-conscious. He hesitated as they approached the square. He was still so young! Some of these men were rough and grizzled fellows who looked as if they had spent a lifetime traveling. How could he pick the guide who would be right for him? Who would even want to work for such an inexperienced, green explorer?

"Son, go. Speak to the men and make your choice. Find someone who will look you in the eye," urged Niccolò.

Marco walked among the men. Some were smoking; others were engaged in conversation with each other or potential employers. Not many took notice of the youngster. Finally, Marco's gaze fell upon a man who was set apart from the crowd, leaning against a stone fence. He wore a wool cape, a fur hat, and held the type of large staff that guides often carried. The man was not especially tall or large, but he held his head high and looked Marco in the eye.

"Good day," he called out.

"Good day," answered Marco. "I'm looking for a guide. I am a merchant, and have been traveling with my father and my uncle."

"But now you are preparing to strike out on your own?" the man asked, smiling. He was not condescending, as Marco had feared an experienced guide would be. This man's attitude was straightforward and without judgment. He really looked to be only a few years older than Marco.

"Yes, soon," said Marco.

The guide studied the young man. "What year were you born?" he asked.

"1254," said Marco, embarrassed to admit his youth.

"Ah. The year of the Tiger." The man smiled as if he were pleased with this information. "I was born in 1250. They tell me that is the year of the Dog. We are a good combination." He bowed. "My name is Gurmi. I am of the Sherpa of Nepal, and am a traveler myself. I would be honored to serve as your guide."

Marco hesitated, but only briefly. Looking in the man's eyes as his father had instructed, he saw strength, honesty and integrity. "Let us make the arrangements," he said eagerly, and the deal was struck.

Gurmi and Marco Polo begin their travels

Marco and his Sherpa guide made trips to Persia and Burma. Marco became a seasoned traveler and an excellent horseman. He and Gurmi worked well together, with Gurmi teaching Marco many things about traveling and Asian culture. As his father had said, the Sherpa was his guide, protector and mentor, but also his friend.

As they traveled, Marco shared with Gurmi the story of his life and the guide told Marco his story as well. He had been orphaned at a young age and had always yearned to travel, like Marco. His feet were never still, Gurmi said, and he was never happier than when on horseback, venturing to a place he had never been.

After more than a year of traveling together, Marco and Gurmi were eager for a rest. They joined Marco's father and uncle at their quarters outside Kublai Khan's Summer Palace, Shangdu. Marco relaxed in a warm bath one afternoon soon after arriving. His muscles were sore and his mind was tired. He was beginning to wonder what it would be like to stay put and work as a city official, as his father and uncle had been doing. His thoughts were interrupted when his father rushed into the room. "Pardon me, Marco," he began hurriedly. "This cannot wait! I have been requesting an audience for you with Kublai Khan, and it has finally been granted. A messenger just came with the news. You are to appear at the palace tonight!"

Marco was instantly energized, his weariness and aches forgotten at the thought of meeting the great Khan. After thanking his father and hurriedly dressing, he made his way to Gurmi's quarters. His guide and friend needed to hear about this.

Gurmi was as excited as Marco about the prospect of meeting Kublai Khan. "He wants to hear about our travels in Persia and Burma," said Marco. "Prepare quickly and accompany me."

The two men were as excited as boys as they made their way to the Summer Palace. At the gate, however, Marco's excitement evaporated into apprehension and his step slowed. The walls surrounding the palace were high mounds of earth and stretched in each direction as far as he could see. The gate itself was tall and wide, made of varnished and gilded cane, sparkling with jewels. A menacing-looking guard armed with a sword stood at the gate, with several men flanking him. Seeing Marco's hesitation, Gurmi approached the guard and spoke.

"This is young Marco Polo, son of Niccolò, and I am his guide, a Sherpa from Nepal. His presence has been requested by the great Kublai Khan."

The guard nodded for two men to open the elaborately decorated gate. He gestured for Marco to precede him. Marco stepped though, but Gurmi did not follow, and as the servants began to close the gate, Marco protested.

"Wait! My guide must accompany me."

"No," said the guard. "The great Khan has requested you alone, not you and a servant."

"He is not my servant," began Marco.

Gurmi interrupted him. "It is only right," he insisted. "You go. I will stay here."

"I will not go without you. It would be a false representation to tell my stories to the Great Khan as if you were not part of them." Marco turned to the guard. "My guide will accompany me, or you may tell the great Kublai Khan that we declined his invitation."

The guard weighed his options, and decided that he would take his chances on admitting the Sherpa guide rather than telling the Khan that the visitors had left. He instructed the gate to be opened again to admit Gurmi. They walked in silence through the courtyards, following the guard. The beauty of the Summer Palace was breathtaking. They passed fountains, brooks, and flowering trees. In the distance could be heard the sweet songs of many birds. Marco took the time during the walk to gather his thoughts and build up his confidence.

"The great Khan is in his Cane Palace," said the guard as they passed a stately building known as the Marble Palace. "It is the only place he finds relief from the midsummer heat."

The Cane Palace was a wonder to behold. Encircled by woods, it was cool and beautiful, with walls and roof of highly lacquered cane. The walls were supported at every corner by gilt dragons and held down against the wind by a multitude of silk cords.

Led by the guard, Marco and Gurmi walked through the gilded halls of the Cane Palace and entered the throne room, where the great Khan was seated at the far end. Marco had regained his courage. He bowed, then immediately spoke. "Great Khan, I am honored to be in your presence. My name is Marco Polo, son of Niccolò. This is my Sherpa guide, Gurmi, without whom I could not have successfully completed my trips to Persia and Burma." He gestured to Gurmi, who bowed low. Kublai Khan was instantly impressed with the young European's forthrightness and integrity. He invited both men to sit, had refreshments brought in, and talked with them for a few hours about their journeys.

"Your father and uncle have settled into their roles here," said the Khan. "They are valuable members of my government. But they no longer desire to travel. I need an explorer to go to the furthest reaches of the Mongol-conquered lands as my emissary. I am impressed by your confidence, and what your father tells me of your skill and intelligence. I want my emissary to be you, Marco Polo. Accompanied, of course, by your worthy guide. And I will provide as many other servants as you need."

Kublai Khan then produced a large gold tablet, oval in shape, and covered with decorations and symbols. "This paiza will serve as a passport. It will be your entry to wherever you travel in my kingdom. It conveys the blessing and favor of Kublai Khan."

Marco bowed low as he accepted the paiza and handed it to his guide. Gurmi read the inscription: "*By the strength of the eternal Heaven, holy be the Khan's name. Let him that pays him not reverence be killed.*"

The golden paiza: passport to the dynasty

"Great Khan, you honor us with your trust," said Marco. "We will endeavor to serve you well on whatever mission you send us."

Kublai Khan's advisors were surprised that he had chosen such a young man to be his emissary. Marco would be in charge of a large ongoing expedition, and would be responsible for many men. But the Khan was impressed with the Europeans he had met, especially this young, intelligent Venetian. And he admired the way Marco respected and honored Gurmi, the Sherpa, as a valued guide.

Kublai Khan was a progressive ruler. He was not only interested in the business prospects of his empire, but delighted in learning how people lived. His goal as a ruler was different than his predecessor, Genghis Khan. Kublai Khan wished to unite China, not crush the conquered regions as previous warriors had done.

The first trip Marco took as the Khan's emissary was to India. Kublai Khan was interested in Marco's thoughts on the possibilities of trade in India, and was also interested in India's religion. Chabi Khatun, the Khan's favorite wife, had convinced him of the merits of Buddhism, and he was eager to learn more about how the religion was practiced in India.

Marco's father and uncle were proud of the impression he had made on the Khan. They helped Marco and his Sherpa guide prepare for the trip. With horses, carts and ten men, Marco and Gurmi set out for India on a bright, chilly morning. The journey was made easier with the possession of the paiza, the golden passport from the great Khan himself. Anyone who was shown the paiza was compelled by order of Kublai Khan to give the travelers food, lodging and safe passage.

It was now 1277. Marco was only twenty-three years old, but he was wise beyond his years, and acted as a confident and intelligent leader. He was also a keen observer. Marco was a merchant, but he had an artist's memory for the sights, sounds, scents and flavors that he encountered on his travels. As an emissary for the Khan, he continued to keep a travel journal, as he had done since he left Venice, and he took daily notes on everything. Descriptions of people and their customs, the vastness of deserts, mountains and plains, and the difficulties of the journey all made their way onto the pages of his journal.

Once in India, Marco was determined to travel the width of the country all the way to the sea. The party of Marco, Gurmi, and the ten porters trudged through hot and cold weather, rain and drought as they traveled across India. They camped in tents and heard many strange sounds at night, including the roars of tigers. As they traveled on horseback near a wooded area, Gurmi explained to Marco that the Bengal tigers in India were not a threat to men. The wild cats kept to themselves unless provoked.

"Well, I have no intention of provoking them," laughed Marco, urging his horse into a trot.

One twilight evening in camp, Gurmi instructed two of the porters to gather wood for a fire. They had not been gone long when Marco and the others heard a commotion.

The two men appeared at the edge of the woods. *"Laohu*! Tigers! Tigers!"* they yelled. Gurmi leapt up, grabbing his bow. He called for the others to join him. All did, except for three cowards who had run for safety in the tents as soon as they heard shouts of fear.

Tigers, out for blood

The trees cast dappled shadows on two great Bengal tigers as they appeared from the trees, fangs bared and growling. One of the men tripped and cried out as the savage cat seized him by the leg and dragged him into the undergrowth. Marco and Gurmi rushed forward, but the other tiger advanced on them, snarling fiercely. Marco brandished his sword, and his Sherpa shot off an arrow which grazed the tiger's back. With a terrible scream, the tiger turned and ran back into the woods. The men watched and waited for a moment, great tension in the air. There was an eerie silence except for the rustling of leaves and branches. The cries of the unfortunate porter who had been dragged into the woods ceased as well. He was surely dead. "Are we safe?" Marco asked Gurmi, turning around to look for other dangers, his sword still in his hand.

"Those tigers have a meal that will keep them satisfied until we are gone tomorrow," answered the Sherpa guide. "Let us build a high fire and keep it burning all night. They are unpredictable, but that will help ensure they do not come back again." Marco and Gurmi lowered their weapons.

Satisfied that the camp would be safe for the night, Marco turned his attention to his men. "Gurmi, gather the porters here," he commanded. Then Marco strode toward the tent where the three men who had bolted when they first heard the cry of 'tiger!' were still hiding. "You! In the tent! Come out and stand before me now!"

The other six porters, led by Gurmi, assembled in front of Marco Polo as well. They were shaken and afraid. None of them had ever seen tigers attack men in this way. Marco addressed them. "Until this day, you have all served me well. Now, one of you has been killed by a renegade tiger. You are all experienced men who know the dangers of traveling. However, if you wish to leave my employ at this point you may do so without loss of honor. Once you return home, my father will see to it that you are paid. Step to the side if you wish to go back."

None of the men stepped aside. They admired Marco Polo and Gurmi and wanted to continue on the journey. But Marco had other ideas for the three cowards.

"You three men who ran when two of your fellow porters were in danger: you will step aside. I no longer wish to have you in my employ. Cowards have no place on this journey. You will sleep with the horses tonight, and begin your journey home at daybreak. I will provide you with a letter to give to my father. He will pay you, but the reason for your return will also be noted, and you will be dishonored."

Without a word, the three guilty men started back to their tents to gather their belongings. Gurmi dismissed the others and turned to Marco. "Master Marco, traveling will be more difficult with fewer porters."

"But those of us who remain will have confidence in the loyalty and bravery of the others," answered Marco.

"Yes. We may move a little slower, but we will sleep better at night."

The group moved on further into India, discovering many wonders along the way. They eventually arrived at a town that housed a Buddhist monastery. Knowing the Khan's interest in Buddhism, Marco wanted to spend some time with the monks. He instructed the porters to care for the horses and find lodging. He and Gurmi made their way to the monastery. The monks greeted them warmly and offered to take them to their caves.

Marco and Gurmi followed the monks to a series of stone caves that were filled with shrines and representations of the Buddha. A sense of stillness and peace filled the caves, each one with more impressive statuary than the last. Finally, they came upon a giant reclining Buddha. "This is most wonderful," whispered Gurmi to Marco as they stood beside the tremendous statue which filled up the entire room of the cave. "It is indeed," answered Marco. He made a drawing of the resting Buddha and wrote a page of notes detailing the majesty of the statue. He was sure the Khan would be interested in it.

The trip to India had already lasted many months, and Marco's notes filled several journals. Marco's pockets were also filling with keepsakes. Leaving the caves, Gurmi saw how the bits of jewelry, small teacups, silk scraps and scrolls weighed down Marco's coat down as he attempted to mount his horse. The guide laughed, and then apologized for the disrespect.

"No, you have given me a thought," said Marco as he emptied his pockets to take inventory. "I have many gifts for the great Khan and some items for my father and uncle as examples of goods for trade. I also have these items, which I want to keep for myself. Along with my journals, they keep my memories alive. But I suppose you are right to laugh at me. Soon enough I will be dragging my robes on the ground, so full they will be of my personal trinkets. I will solve this problem tonight."

At the monastery, Marco found some fine sturdy wood, colorful leather, metal straps, and the tools he needed to build a chest. With the help of several of the monks who were skilled craftsmen, he built a magnificent chest. One of the monks even painted an illustration of Marco and Gurmi on the front of the chest, and decorated the sides, back and top with pictures as well. "This is what will hold my personal items," he said to Gurmi proudly as he polished the lid and tested the hinges. "You will be in charge of transporting this chest and ensuring its safety. I will carry a list of the items stored in it."

After Marco emptied the items from his coat and robes into the chest, the Sherpa guide peeked inside. He saw a collection of Marco's journals, and many of the keepsakes and trinkets collected on their travels. "Good. It is large enough to hold much more," the guide said with a smile. "You are fortunate I have the muscles and the good will to carry it!"

"I have many stories to tell the great Khan when we return," countered Marco. "These keepsakes will help me remember and embellish my tales. Kublai Khan loves a good story. This chest will travel the length and breadth of the Yuan Dynasty. So take care of my Dynasty chest, Gurmi. It will be filled with good stories."

"Grandpa, that sounds like a life chest!" said April excitedly. "Marco Polo made a life chest, didn't he?"

"He didn't call it a life chest, but that's pretty much what it was. And wait till you hear about what he put in it next, after he went back to Kublai Khan's palace. Want me to read more?"

"Yes, Grandpa!" said April. "Please," she quickly added.

"My pleasure," said Josh, smiling as he turned back to the book.

Kublai Khan did love a good story. He was pleased with both the trade reports and the fantastic tales that Marco brought from India. The story of the reclining Buddha in the cave was the one that impressed him the most. Kublai Khan was fascinated with all religions and had even learned about Christianity from the Europeans. He told a story of his own after Marco had told him about the reclining Buddha they had seen in India.

"There is also a reclining Buddha here, in Zhangye, in the giant Buddha Temple. My mother gave birth to me in that Temple. I had not known of a similar Buddha in all the world. The news you bring gives me hope that this vast kingdom can be united." The great Khan was silent for a moment, deep in thought. Then he spoke again. "Marco Polo, your service to me is invaluable. Remain here in my palace for three weeks. At the end of that time, return for another audience. You will be rewarded for your service."

Marco was glad to have the chance to rest in the beautiful palace of Kublai Khan. When he was summoned back into the Khan's presence, he saw what he had been waiting three weeks for. Kublai Khan motioned Marco to approach his throne. Marco saw a large gold disk in his hand. The Khan held it up.

The gold coins: a priceless treasure

"I have had my personal goldsmith working day and night these past three weeks. This is the result of his work," said the ruler. He handed Marco the disk. It was a heavy gold coin about four inches in diameter and a quarter inch thick, with an ornate border. He also had a covered basket, and lifted the lid so Marco could see inside. The basket was full of the gold coins. "There are fifty coins in total, wrought in a unique design. They are my gift to you for your fine work as my emissary. The Yuan Dynasty is thriving in large part because of your assistance."

Marco was overwhelmed. "Thank you, Great Khan, for your generosity. I will continue to do my best in your service."

"That is good to hear. You have become invaluable to me as an emissary. Your next trip will be to Tibet. Ask my servants for anything you need as you prepare."

Marco bowed low. A servant handed him the basket of coins. He left Kublai Khan's presence amazed and grateful. The fifty gold coins soon became part of the riches held by the Dynasty chest. Marco had each coin wrapped in a small piece of leather, and put the entire treasure in a sturdy box.

Gurmi made transporting and caring for the Dynasty chest and the precious coins one of his main priorities. While resting in their tent at night while on an expedition, he and Marco both enjoyed looking through the items in the chest and recalling the stories of their adventures.

On one of their journeys, Marco, Gurmi and several porters set out from Dadu to check on conditions in the central and southern cities following a series of earthquakes. After about four weeks' travel and the inspection of several villages, they found themselves outside the city of Chang'an.

It was late in the day, and Marco decided to stop for the night. Gurmi instructed the porters to set up camp in a fallow field with a stream nearby. The horses were taken care of first, and while the tents were being set up and food prepared, Marco took a walk around the area. The fields were flat, but there were craggy hills in the distance, with bright green strips of trees illuminated by shafts of afternoon sun. It looked as if this region, seemingly peaceful and quiet, had not been affected by the earthquakes. Marco turned away from the view of the distant peaks to head back to camp. His foot hit something hard and he almost tripped. Curious, he bent down to see what it was. Maybe the earth had shifted here after all, and stones had cropped up in these farmers' fields. What he picked up wasn't a stone, however. It was a broken piece of unglazed pottery about six inches long, curved like a section of pipe. Marco wondered what it was. Part of a vase? A clay pipe for some kind of irrigation system?

The men were seated around the fire when he returned to camp. "Master Marco," called Gurmi. "I have brewed your tea."

"Thank you," said Marco, sitting and taking the cup. "Here, look at this piece of pottery. Can you tell what it is? Why do you think it was out in the middle of the field?" He handed it to Gurmi, who passed it to the porters. One of the men jumped up with a gasp when he saw the pottery piece.

"This thing is cursed!" he said. "It belongs to the ghosts!"

"Ghosts?" asked Marco. "What do you mean?"

The man explained. "My father lived in this area as a boy. He told me many stories about these fields. Men would often find pieces of pottery when building a family tomb or plowing the land. Some pieces were flat, and some were curved like this one. My father told me that one fragment looked like part of a man's face. The farmer who found that piece died the next day. He said there was no explanation for it except that the fields were possessed. That must be the reason this field has not been planted with wheat. It has been given up to the ghosts."

Marco was amazed by the story. "Do farmers really abandon their fields to appease ghosts?" he asked.

"They take it very seriously," the man assured him. "Many believe that there are whole cities of ghosts living underground. We may be on top of one here."

The rest of the porters nodded in agreement. In fact, several of the men became nervous about the idea of sleeping above a ghost city, and insisted on moving camp. The man who told the story started to shake with fear. Gurmi stood and held up his hand.

"The ghosts will not bother us if we do not disturb them. I will return the piece of pottery to where it was found, and I believe we will be able to camp here safely."

Marco stood as well. "I will show you where I found it, so we can return it to its proper place. The ghosts will understand that we mean them no harm."

After a bit of grumbling, the porters were satisfied that this plan would appease the ghosts. Marco and his Sherpa guide started toward the field where Marco had found the pottery piece, shielding their eyes against the low afternoon rays of the sun.

"Do you think you can find the exact spot where you picked up the pottery shard?" asked Gurmi as they walked.

"Probably not," admitted Marco. "But I think we can get close enough for the ghosts." He turned to look at his trusted guide. "Do you believe the stories yourself?"

"I have heard a lot of ghost stories over the years," said the Sherpa. "And I have some ancestors who would be quite angry to have people tromping over their graves. So I do not mind going out of my way to make these ghosts happy."

"You are a wise man, Gurmi," said Marco. He stopped. "I think we are close enough to the spot. Let us leave the pottery piece here. I still wonder what it is."

Marco's thoughts were interrupted by a loud rumble. There was no chance to set the pottery piece down. It flew out of Marco's hand as the ground began to shake beneath them. It was an earthquake!

Both men were thrown to the ground. The sensation was like being on the deck of a rolling ship. After a moment, the silty soil gave way beneath them. Marco and his Sherpa guide felt themselves falling into a hole opened up by the quake. Dirt fell all around them, choking out the light and threatening to choke out their breath as well. Marco and Gurmi covered their faces with their arms and tried to protect themselves from debris. They crawled away from the falling earth as best they could. The quake continued, threatening to close the opening that Marco and Gurmi had tumbled into, trapping them underground. After a few minutes, the shaking finally subsided and the dust began to settle. The shifting earth had not completely covered the hole, and there was still air to breathe.

"Master Marco?" called Gurmi.

"I am unhurt. Are you?" answered Marco.

"I have twisted my foot, but I can stand."

Marco attempted to wipe the dust from his eyes. He was sitting on hard packed earth, and there seemed to be walls of the same packed dirt on either side of him. The space between the two walls of earth made a sort of corridor. Split and rotting timbers, forming a rough ceiling, hung above his head. The earthquake had uncovered some kind of pit or cave, and they had fallen into it! Marco saw Gurmi limping toward him, and stood to help the injured man.

"Master Marco, what—?" The guide did not finish his sentence. He crumpled to the ground in a heap, pointing past Marco's head. At first Marco thought Gurmi's foot injury had worsened, but then he turned around, following his guide's shaking finger.

He stared into the face of a man. A soldier, who stood straight and tall before him. Marco's hand went to the jeweled dagger at his side. "I am armed!" he called. The soldier did not move a muscle. Marco rubbed more dirt out of his eyes, blinked, and looked around. He could see now that the figure was some kind of statue. And there was more than one. Four were lined up facing him. Past the first line of soldiers, there was another line, and another, and another, filling the packed earth corridor in ranks of four, as far as he could see in the dusty shadows. Gurmi scrambled to his feet and tried to speak. "It is the ghosts," he whispered hoarsely. "We are done for!"

Marco comes face to face with a terracotta "ghost"

Marco heard the panic in his guide's voice and began to feel it himself. Could these figures really be ghosts, and would they seek vengeance for this invasion of their resting place? No! Of course not! Marco took a deep breath and tried to think rationally. Whatever the figures were, the more important problem was getting out of the pit. He crossed himself as he turned to Gurmi, and hoped that he sounded confident. "In the name of all that is holy, we must find a way out of here. Ghosts or not, there may be another earthquake. Then we would certainly be done for!"

Gurmi knew Marco was right, and tried to control his fear. Hopefully they could find a place to climb out of the pit. The dust had settled a bit more, and as the men looked around, they saw several broken figures at their feet, crushed in the earthquake. Marco picked up a limb. "They are not ghosts, unless ghosts are made of clay," he said, turning the piece over to examine it. "The pottery shard I found in the field must have been part of an arm like this. This is an army regiment, all made of clay!" Marco held up the severed arm to show Gurmi, but the guide was not interested in examining any part of the clay soldiers. He didn't want to escape the pit only to die the next day, like the unfortunate farmer who had found the clay face!

There was a shaft of light penetrating the pit, even though the earthquake had largely covered the hole they had fallen into. Gurmi started to pick his way through the rubble toward the light, and Marco followed. As they moved toward the opening, they began to hear frantic voices from above. The porters had left camp after the earthquake to search for Marco and Gurmi, and were calling their names.

"We are here!" yelled Marco. "The earthquake dropped us down into this pit!"

The porters dropped a rope through the hole. Marco insisted that Gurmi be pulled up first, since he had been injured. The guide winced as the porters dragged him to safety. As Marco waited for the rope to be tossed down to him, he turned back toward the corridor, filled with orderly rows of silent clay soldiers. There was a sense of mystery and grandeur that intrigued the explorer. What a discovery!

"Master Marco!" called Gurmi from above. "Do you have the rope?"

Before Marco answered, he took one last look at the ranks of clay soldiers in their silent majesty. He then reached down to the pottery shards at his feet and picked up a small piece of a soldier's breastplate. He slid it into a pocket and grabbed the rope. "Pull!" he yelled, looking up to the light.

Gurmi sighed with relief when Marco was safe above ground. "Master Marco, I was beginning to think that the ghosts were trying to keep you in the pit."

"Don't worry. They wouldn't want me." Marco laughed.

The porters, however, were in no mood for jokes. Not only were they terrified of the possibility of more earthquakes, they demanded to know more about this mention of ghosts. "Let us make our way back to camp," said Marco. "There is no need for fear." The group began to walk back to their tents and horses, but the men were still not satisfied.

"You should have listened to me!" said the porter who had first told the others about the ghosts in the field. "We are in danger here!"

The others joined in. "What was in the pit?" they asked anxiously. "Were you attacked by ghosts?" Their fear escalated. "We have made the ghosts angry!" one cried out. "They caused the earthquake, and will strike us with another if we stay here!" another insisted.

Marco tried to quell the rising panic among the men. "We are on a mission from the great Khan. We are obligated to complete it!" he insisted.

"But even the Khan cannot protect us from earthquakes," said Gurmi. "Whether they are caused by ghosts or not, perhaps it would be best to leave this area."

"I suppose you are right, Gurmi," Marco admitted reluctantly. The porters agreed to stay through the night as long as they broke camp at daybreak. Very few of them slept, and Marco dreamed over and over again of being eye to eye with a silent, menacing clay soldier.

As soon as the sun appeared on the horizon, the porters broke camp. The expedition headed back to Dadu and the Imperial

Palace. Marco was disappointed at not being able to investigate the pit further. He was an explorer, and this was an incredible find. He was also concerned about having to explain to Kublai Khan why the trip was cut short.

Back at the Imperial Palace, Marco told Kublai Khan what the earthquake had uncovered. He need not have worried; the great Khan was glad they were back. "It was wise of you to return," the Khan said. "I have no wish to disturb the ghosts of ancient ancestors. Let it not be said that the Mongols conquered China only to desecrate sacred ground."

Secretly, Kublai Khan was gripped by as much fear as Marco's porters. His army was stretched thin as it was, fighting rebellions in the south. What if his enemies found out about these ghost soldiers and used sorcery to call them to action? What if a ghost army should rise up against him? There would be no way to defeat an army of spirits. He spoke again.

"Marco Polo, everything you have told me this day must be kept secret. Years ago, I heard of an ancient army of terracotta soldiers. They numbered in the thousands. I had thought it was a myth. Now we know it truly exists. Upon pain of death, no one must talk of what you discovered. Your guide and porters will be paid for their silence." He held out his hand. "Approach and give me the book in which you record the findings of your journeys."

One did not argue with the great Kublai Khan. Marco silently handed his journal to the ruler, who carefully examined the last several pages. "Your account of the journey begins here?" he asked. Marco nodded. The Khan called for a sharp blade and carefully removed the last ten pages of Marco's journal. He handed the book back to Marco and said, "You will take this secret to your grave." He gestured to his guards to escort Marco from the throne room. Marco bowed and left, disappointed in losing the record of his great discovery, but relieved that he remained in the Khan's good graces.

A few weeks later, reports arrived of more earthquakes in the area of Chang'an. Damage was said to be severe. Marco wondered if the army of clay had been destroyed, forever lost to the ravages of nature. Perhaps he was the last man to look in the eyes of the mysterious soldiers. The pottery shard he had taken from the pit, hidden in the Dynasty chest, was the sole evidence of the adventure.

Over the next several years, Marco and Gurmi continued to travel through the lands of the Yuan Dynasty on behalf of Kublai Khan. The golden paiza, the passport of the Khan, was invaluable in securing them shelter, food and passage along the way. Marco enjoyed the life of the adventurer, and filled the Dynasty chest with trinkets and treasures. However, after a total of nineteen years in the East, he longed to return home.

Niccolò and Matteo wanted to leave as well. They had accumulated great wealth in gold, jewels and unusual items for trade, and were eager to go back to Italy and resume their business as merchants. They were also worried that if the aging Khan, who had been their friend and protector, were to die, they might not be allowed to leave with their riches. Kublai Khan was reluctant to see them go, but he needed their sailing expertise for a journey to Persia which would bring a Mongol princess to her wedding. After some negotiating, the great Khan finally agreed to let the Polos depart in 1292.

Marco, now thirty-eight years old, had not been home to Italy for many years. He was eager to go back, but he and Gurmi had become close friends; almost brothers. It was difficult for either of them to imagine life without the other. But Marco's trip home would mean the end of their travels together.

Gurmi knew that Marco would not ask him to go on this last journey. But the Sherpa guide admired and loved his friend. If their travels together were going to come to an end, at least he wanted to see him safely home as far as possible. He told Marco that he would join the party to escort the princess to Persia. "After all," he said, "who will carry your Dynasty chest if not your faithful guide?"

With the cargo and the ships prepared, the party traveled first to Sumatra. They were detained there by monsoons for several months. Bandits roamed the land and tried several times to board their ships in port. In one instance they were almost successful. A few bandits managed to get past the guards and down into a hold where they made away with several casks of jewels.

The Polos were frustrated at the state of things. Their ships were docked in the port of Sumatra, helpless as sitting ducks. They had nothing to depend on but their own vigilance. It would only be a matter of time before they were attacked again, likely by more desperate bandits wielding heavier weapons.

Marco came to a decision. Early one morning, he instructed Gurmi to wrap the Dynasty chest in rough cloth and load it onto a cart. With the cart, the two men left the port area and traveled a mile or so outside of the town. Marco wanted this project to be kept secret from everyone except his trusted guide. In the shade of a grove of palm trees, Marco gave Gurmi instructions as he removed tools from a pack. All the objects in the Dynasty chest were important, but the fifty gold coins, the gift from Kublai Khan, were by far the most valuable.

Building a false bottom in the Dynasty chest to hide the coins

After emptying out the chest, Gurmi constructed a false bottom for it, guided by Marco's instructions. Underneath the false bottom they lined up the coins, each still wrapped in leather, in ten rows of five.

They talked as they packed the rest of the objects back into the chest on top of the false bottom. "I'm confident that the coins are well hidden," said Marco. "As for disguising the chest itself, once back on the ship we will keep it wrapped in this burlap. I will hide it in a crate of onions."

"And don't let anyone eat the onions," added the clever Gurmi. "The more they rot the better."

"Eww. Stinky. I don't like onions," offered April.

"Neither does your grandma," said Josh. "No. Correction: she doesn't like kissing me when I have raw onions on my breath, is all."

April giggled. "Did they really hide the chest under onions, Grandpa?"

"They didn't get a chance to. Here's what happened next." Josh turned the page.

Marco and the Sherpa guide walked back to the port, confident that they had done their best to protect the Kahn's gift. As they approached the port where the Polos' ships were docked, what they heard and saw gave them a sense of dread that quickly turned to horror.

Several bandits were approaching the ships. Some were already on board. The travelers were being attacked again, and the bandits were well armed with swords and knives. They had heard of the treasure on board the ships and were ready to kill to get their hands on it.

Gurmi hid the cart underneath a shrub. He and Marco quickly decided on a plan of action. They would sneak up on the bandits who were still approaching, and attack them from behind. If they could stop any more thieves from boarding, the men on board might be able to successfully defend themselves.

Marco had a saber but Gurmi carried only his fighting staff. Wielded by someone with martial arts training, however, the staff could be deadly, and he was skilled in its use.

The two men stealthily moved toward the bandits. Two "bandits" were on the main ship's gangplank, fighting three men. Two others were just onshore, waiting to board the ship. Their attention was focused on the activity in front of them, so Marco and Gurmi were able to surprise them with their attack from behind. The Sherpa took both men down with one blow of his staff and Marco killed them with his saber.

"Take one of their swords," urged Marco, but Gurmi declined. "My staff will serve me best today," he insisted. "Besides, there is no time. The others are upon us!"

The men who had been fighting on the gangplank had turned their attention to Marco and Gurmi, and rushed down toward them. Marco advanced on them and made it halfway up the gangplank, brandishing his saber and yelling, "You cursed bandits! You will see death at the end of my sword!"

The bandits had solid footing further up on the gangplank, but Marco tripped and stumbled as he was running. Struggling to retain his balance, he looked up to see the glint of a bandit's saber in the sun as the blade came down toward him. Then—had he completely lost his balance or was it something else that toppled him over the edge of the gangplank? He fell into the water with a splash. Standing where he had been was Gurmi, who had indeed pushed him in with one end of his staff. In the same motion, he slammed the bandit across the throat with the other end.

Choking in pain and anger, the bandit struck upwards with his sword, catching the underside of the Sherpa's staff as he was bringing it back down again on the bandit's shoulder. The bandit's sword sliced through Gurmi's right wrist, completely severing his hand. Before he could even feel the pain, Gurmi used his last ounce of strength to land a deadly blow to the bandit's temple, holding onto his staff with his left hand. As the body crashed to the gangplank, Marco pulled himself up in time to see his friend and guide fall to his knees, clutching the stump of his bleeding arm.

The rest of the bandits were quickly defeated by the crew, as their leader was the one who had been killed by Gurmi's staff. Marco helped bring Gurmi aboard the ship. The ship's doctor tended to him immediately. Marco stole back to shore to retrieve the Dynasty chest.

There were many injuries and a few deaths resulting from the skirmish with the bandits. The Polos and their crew were on constant guard against further attempts to board their ships and steal their wealth. Thankfully, they were soon able to leave Sumatra and resume the journey to Persia. Gurmi was bedridden and feverish, but it was believed he would live. As he gained strength and began to recover, Marco spent many hours with him. He kept the Dynasty chest in Gurmi's quarters. Taking items out to show his friend, Marco told and retold the stories of their travels through China, Burma, Tibet and India. They held a compass and a brass quadrant while they recalled a grueling trip through the desert. They lifted two black jade dragons from the chest and remembered the majesty of the great Khan's palaces.

As they approached the next port, Gurmi told Marco it was time for him to turn back. "I will be returning to China now that I have recovered my health. It has been my privilege to serve as your guide these many years. I know I will not find another adventurer with your intelligence and integrity."

"So will you now find yourself a wife and retire to the country?" laughed Marco.

"It does sound like a fine possibility," answered Gurmi. "If I can find a woman who will marry a man who possesses no right hand."

Marco's mood turned sober. "You lost your hand in saving my life. I can gift you with jade and jewels but I cannot replace your hand."

"There is nothing about my life and my service to you that I would alter, I assure you," said Gurmi.

"I must thank you for your service," insisted Marco. "Anything I would give you is a weak representation of my gratitude, but I will give you the best that I have in the hope that it expresses even half my thanks." He opened the Dynasty chest. "This chest and all the things in it represent my life and my memories of China these past twenty years, from when I was nineteen to now almost forty years of age. I will take my journals, some jewels and a few pieces of jade, but the chest and everything else in it will go back with you. Here is the paiza, the golden passport given to us by the great Khan. It is of no use to me anymore, but it will help you in your journey back. It may be useful for generations to come. The hidden treasure will be yours as well."

"Master Marco, I cannot take the Dynasty chest! I cannot take the gold coins—"

The Dynasty chest: passed from Marco to his guide

"You must. Even with the coins hidden in the false bottom of the chest, there is no guarantee that they will be safe from bandits and robbers during the rest of my journey home. You will keep the legacy, my friend. I will use my journals to remember, and you will use the treasures in this chest to remember the stories and hand them down to your descendants. You are going to find a wife when you return to China, remember?"

"Yes, and I will have children. I will tell them the story of Marco Polo and share with them the treasures of the Dynasty chest. Except the coins; they will remain our secret, at least for now. But the Dynasty chest will be passed down to many future generations. I promise this to you, my lifelong master and friend." Gurmi closed the chest, closed a chapter of his life, and waited for the next chapter to open.

Josh closed the book, yawned and stretched. "Well, Blossom, now you know who Marco Polo was."

"But Grandpa, what happened after that? Did the Sherpa guide get married and have kids? Did Marco Polo make it back home?"

"Yes and yes, Blossom. There are lots more adventures with the Dynasty chest that aren't in this book. I can tell you those stories another time."

"Grandpa, how do you know those stories?"

"Bernie and I read the journals we found in Great-Great-Grandpa Kim's life chest. He wrote down tons of stories that he got from a friend of his in Thailand. It takes a lot of work to keep these stories alive, but it's worth it. Did you know that Marco Polo recorded all of his stories when he was locked up in prison?"

"Why was he in prison? Did he do something bad?"

"No, he was just on the unlucky side in a war. What was lucky, though, was that he was in prison with a writer, who made sure all his stories got put down on paper."

"He told him everything, Grandpa? Even the secret about the gold coins in the Dynasty chest?"

"Maybe, Blossom. Marco's stories were so amazing that a lot of people who read them thought he was making them up. Even now, people argue about whether his stories were true. If he told people about the coins, they probably didn't believe him anyway."

"I would have believed him," said April, crossing her arms in defiance of the naysayers.

"Good for you, Blossom. Next time I see you, I'll tell you the stories of who had the Dynasty chest after the Sherpa guide." Josh looked up and sniffed. "Hey, I think I smell brownies. Do you? Let's see if Grandma made them with chocolate chips!" He stood and reached for the button that opened the sliding door.

April wasn't done with her questions, however. "Wait a minute, Grandpa," she said. "You told me that Kublai Khan tore up Marco's story about the clay soldiers and ordered him never to talk about them. If that part of the story wasn't in his book, how do you know about it?" Josh paused in the doorway. "Grandpa," April said suspiciously. "Are you making up stories as you go along?"

"Who, me?" said Josh with wide innocent eyes. "Why, Blossom! Are you saying you don't like my stories?"

"Of course I like them, Grandpa. But—"

"Last one to the kitchen is a rotten egg!" laughed Josh as he ran down the hall.

"Hey, no fair! You got a head start!" called April as she chased after him. Marco Polo was forgotten in favor of brownies.

THE LIFE CHEST

— Chapter 2 —

Six Generations:

The Dynasty Chest is Filled

Just after the New Year, April was sick with a bad cold. She was restless and wanted to get up, but the doctor said she needed to stay in bed for a few days. Josh came over to visit. He figured he could distract her by telling her some more stories about the Dynasty chest. Meg, April's mom, was glad to take a break for a few hours and do some shopping.

"Thanks for coming over, Dad," said Meg at the door of April's bedroom. "April's been cranky all morning, but she's excited to see you. She's had her medicine, and there's chicken soup in the fridge if she's hungry."

"Sounds good," said Josh. "Now go sit at the coffee shop with a latte!"

Meg laughed. "You know me too well." She called back into April's room as she picked up her keys at the door. "Bye, honey!"

The formerly cranky April perked up as soon as her grandpa came in the room. "Yay! You're here!"

"How are you feeling, Blossom?" asked Josh.

"Better now, Grandpa."

"Good. Look what I brought to show you." He held up a large jade figurine of a sinewy black dragon. "I keep it in my life chest. Your Great-Uncle Bernie has one just like it."

"Wow, Grandpa," said April. "It's neat. Where did you get it?"

"Well, believe it or not, it's originally from the Dynasty chest. I can tell you a few stories today about people who kept the chest over the years."

"You mean Marco Polo's Dynasty chest?" asked April excitedly. "Where is the chest now? What happened to it? Are the gold coins still in it?"

"Hold it, hold it," laughed Josh. "I don't want to get ahead of myself in the story. Now give me a minute here. I know these stories pretty well, but it's been a while since I read Gramps' old journals."

"Who's Gramps?" interrupted April.

"My Great-Great-Grandpa Kim. He's the one that wrote down a lot of these stories when he heard them and put them in his life chest, remember? In fact, he's the one that started the whole life chest tradition and business."

"What gave him the idea?" asked April.

"When he was a young man, he saw the original Dynasty chest, the one that Marco Polo built and gave to his Sherpa guide. Gramps was friends with a man who was a descendant of the guide. That man was the family's chest keeper. He was responsible for the Dynasty chest, along with a lot of other chests from members of their family."

"That's a big responsibility," said April. Then she sneezed and Josh reached for a tissue.

April blew her nose while Josh continued. "Now Blossom, you're making me get ahead of myself again," said Josh. "If we're going to do this, let's do it right."

Josh had read the Dynasty chest stories from Gramps' journal many times over the years. He was excited to pass the tales on to his granddaughter, and he wanted her to remember the occasion. Telling the stories was a chance to pass on life lessons, too. "This needs to be special," he declared. "Let's see. If I'm going to put on my official storyteller hat, then I need an actual hat. What do you have?" He stood and looked around the room.

"My dress-up clothes are there," said April, pointing to a purple toy box. She giggled. "Grandpa, are you really going to wear one of my hats?"

"Of course," said Josh as he rummaged through the costumes. "How about this tiara?" He tried it on. "No, it's not really me. These bunny ears aren't quite right, either. Ah, here we go." Josh pulled out a black felt pirate hat from among the princess dresses and space suits. He smoothed out the wrinkles and plopped it on his head. "Perfect. This is now my official storyteller hat." April clapped and laughed.

Josh sat on the edge of the bed. "Okay, where was I? Let's go back to after the Sherpa guide got the Dynasty chest from Marco Polo. It was the year 1292, I think. He went back to China and got married, like Marco Polo thought he would. He was pretty well known by then, being the best friend of Marco Polo and all."

"I guess he would be!" said April.

Josh smiled. "Anyway, he had the Dynasty chest and all the treasures in it, but he married a Chinese woman who was already wealthy, so he kept those gold coins hidden in the bottom of the chest. I guess he figured he'd save them for a rainy day. What he really wanted was a lot of children. So, after he and his new wife had their first meal together, he put the chopsticks they had used in the Dynasty chest. They weren't anything special; they were just made of bamboo. But chopsticks are a symbol of having children quickly, so he hoped that putting them in the dynasty chest would bring good luck. He also put a tortoise shell in the chest. That's a symbol of long life and health, since tortoises live a long time."

"Did it work, Grandpa?" asked April. "Did they have a lot of babies?"

"I guess it did work. They had a baby girl the very next year, and twin boys after that."

"Oh, I wish I had twin brothers!" said April. "That would be so much fun!"

"You might not think so after you hear about these two boys," said Josh, laughing. "Now, settle back on your pillow and I'll tell you what happened. No more interruptions, Blossom. I'm in serious storyteller mode now!" Josh adjusted the pirate hat and began.

Liu Bao Yu means precious jade, and their first baby, born in 1294, was very precious to Gurmi and his wife. Liu Bao Yu was a sweet, quiet baby, so her parents were not prepared for the fussy, loud twins that were born two years later. Liu Bao Yu loved sitting on her father's lap to look at items from the Dynasty chest and hear stories. But her brothers didn't have the patience to sit still and listen to stories. They were always running, playing, fighting and making noise.

Gurmi watched his children as they grew. They were happy and well cared for, but he marveled at how children from the same parents could be so different. The twins were not bad boys, but they were loud, rowdy and undisciplined. They quarreled a lot, and when they weren't quarreling, they were playing pranks. Liu Bao Yu, on the other hand, grew up to be a quiet, responsible and thoughtful girl. She was very helpful to her mother and was patient with her little brothers. She even enjoyed their antics. It got so that it was no longer fun for the boys to tease her because she was so good-natured about it.

Liu Bao Yu was always asking questions. She was interested in learning about her ancestors and loved worshipping at the family shrine with her parents. She especially liked learning about the precious items in the Dynasty chest, and she would sit for hours while her father told her stories of his adventures with Marco Polo.

After one evening of telling stories to his daughter, Gurmi thought about the future of the Dynasty chest. He wanted to make sure it was valued and protected after his death. His first thought was that he would give his oldest son the responsibility. But he had these two boys, the twins who often quarreled and were jealous of each other. He could pick the one that was born first to be keeper of the Dynasty chest. But would he take it seriously? And would there be more jealousy and quarreling?

Then he thought of his daughter, his oldest child. She certainly had the qualities to take on the responsibility of the Dynasty chest. Gurmi came to a decision. It didn't matter if she was a girl. His oldest child would become the keeper of the Dynasty chest. He breathed a little easier, knowing that Liu Bao Yu would honor the responsibility. After that, the tradition was set. Boy or girl, the oldest child would always have the responsibility of guarding the Dynasty chest.

Gurmi still kept up some habits from his old days as Marco Polo's guide. Because they were always hiding treasures from possible bandits when he and Marco were journeying together, he had a tendency to hide things around the house, too. Sometimes it annoyed his wife, but she mostly shook her head and smiled when she saw a stash of his favorite tea hidden under a pile of sleeping mats, or his best chopsticks on a ledge above the door.

Gurmi also added more secret compartments to the Dynasty chest. It already had the false bottom, but he put in slats of thin wood to make false sides as well. He extended the molding around the rim of the chest to cover the false sides. When it was finished, he slipped some paper money and a few rubies and sapphires into the false sides.

One afternoon when his daughter Liu Bao Yu was twelve years old, Gurmi called her to the family shrine room where the

Dynasty chest was kept. "Daughter," he said solemnly, "I have something important to tell you. After I die, I want you to be responsible for the Dynasty chest."

"Father, you are not going to die for a long time," Liu Bao Yu said.

"Heaven willing, that is true," her father answered. "But I want you to hear this now. I have decided that my oldest child will bear this responsibility. You will do well as the Dynasty chest keeper. You will honor its legacy and keep its treasures safe. When you die, you will hand down the responsibility to your oldest child in turn."

"It will be an honor, Father," said Liu Bao Yu as she bowed.

Gurmi picked up a small box. "I have a gift for you," he said. "It represents your thoughtfulness and your constant striving for goodness and enlightenment." He handed the box to his daughter. She turned it over in her hand. It was red, highly lacquered, with an intricate carving of a dragon on the lid. She opened the box. Inside was a single pearl, glowing white in its perfection.

"Like the dragon chasing a beautiful pearl, you seek after knowledge and enlightenment," said Gurmi. "I hope you will always do so."

"I will keep this gift in the Dynasty chest as a reminder," said his daughter. "Thank you, Father."

Gurmi showed his daughter one of the false sides he had built in the Dynasty chest. He lifted the molding, placed the box with the pearl in the compartment, and closed it. "See? The little box fits perfectly into the secret compartment I have made."

"Oh, Father," she smiled. "You and your secret compartments."

"A secret compartment is a valuable thing to have even when you're not being chased by bandits. Just think, if your little brothers sneak in and search around in the Dynasty chest, they won't be able to find your pearl."

"That is true, Father," agreed Liu Bao Yu. "If we can ever get them to sit still, you can show them some of your treasures and tell them about the Dynasty chest. You could start with the story of how you saved Marco Polo's life, and—" she stopped, not knowing if her father really wanted to tell that story.

"And lost my hand?" Gurmi finished the thought. "Yes, I did lose my hand saving Master Marco's life. And I would do it again. It's all right to talk about it. After we eat our evening meal tonight, I will set your brothers down if I have to tie them up. I'll show them the jeweled dagger that Marco Polo carried. But I won't reveal all the secrets of the Dynasty chest to them. I may not even reveal all of them to you," he added, giving his daughter a mischievous look.

"Whatever you say, Father," Liu Bao Yu answered, wondering what other secrets the Dynasty chest might hold.

"And that's the first story, Blossom," said Josh.

"What secret was Gurmi talking about, Grandpa?" asked April excitedly. "The gold coins?"

"You guessed it," said Josh. He pulled the pirate hat down over one eye. "Now here's story number two."

Thirteen years later, Liu Bao Yu smiled at her baby son. The little boy, named Tan Bang, was happily smooshing his fingers into a bowl of mashed mango that his father had given him. It was his first birthday and a time of great celebration.

Her parents, her brothers, and her husband's family were all at the party. After drinking a glass of wine, Liu Bao Yu's twin brothers jumped up from the table, yelling and clapping. "Time for the grabbing test! The baby must do the grabbing test!"

They searched the house to find the best objects for the test. This was an important milestone in a Chinese child's life. The game was done to get an idea of what the baby's future would be. Little Tan Bang was set down on the floor, with a half circle of objects all carefully placed within his grasp. The one that Tan Bang picked up and held onto would give the family a clue as to his future.

"Qiǎng! Qiǎng! (Grab, grab!)" shouted the uncles. "Pick the toy dragon!" called one.

"Hush," reprimanded their father. "Let the child concentrate."

Tan Bang looked around at his relatives and then at the objects that were placed before him. There was a mango. If he picked that, he would be a stodgy, lazy man. If he picked the book, he would be a scholar. There was a family name seal. If he chose that, it meant he would have a career as a government official. If he picked up scissors, his mother would take them from him quickly. But besides that, it would mean his future career would be a tailor. If he picked the toy, he would be a happy-go-lucky drifter. The family excitedly watched as Tan Bang reached for one object, then another. But his chubby hand finally rested on the wooden rectangular seal, with a tiger carved into its top. He picked it up, waved it in the air, and began to chew on it.

His family cheered. "Hooray! Tan Bang will become a highly esteemed government official. His mother and father will be very proud of him."

Liu Bao Yu picked up her baby and exchanged the seal for the dragon toy, which he put into his mouth as well. "It is a good outcome," she said.

"Now let us feast!" said her husband. "My son will be successful and prosperous."

It was more than three decades later when Tan Bang held the seal in his hand again. His own son had just been born, and he and his mother were reminiscing, looking at items in the Dynasty chest. His mother, Liu Bao Yu, had been the keeper of the Dynasty chest for almost four years, since her father died.

"Our family has more valuable seals than this one," Tan Bang said as he looked at the old wooden seal with the tiger carving. "Why have you kept this one in the Dynasty chest?"

His mother laughed. "Don't you see the teeth marks on it? That is what you picked in the grabbing test when you were a year old. I never told you because I didn't want you to think that we would force you to become a government official. But you did! You scored well on the Imperial examinations and have been very successful."

"I hope it was the right career choice for me, Mother," Tan Bang sighed. "Some of the men I work with are not honest. They steal from their superiors and lie to their clients. They pressure me to do the same. I am afraid I will not receive a promotion unless I do as they ask."

Liu Bao Yu did not speak. She held out her hand and her son placed the wooden seal in it. She turned it over, thinking, and finally looked up at her son. "My son, I believe that when you chose this seal in the grabbing test that you were not only choosing your future profession. You were choosing to live a life of honor. This seal is inscribed with your family's name. If you have no money, no property, no possessions, you still have the honor of our family's name. That is more important than anything else. Show yourself to be a man of honor and integrity and your superiors will see it. You will achieve the promotions you deserve."

"Thank you for your wise counsel, Mother," said Tan Bang. "I will take it to heart, believe me. Now, I wonder what my son will pick in the grabbing test one year from today?"

"I hope he will pick a book," answered his mother. "I would love to have a scholar in the family to discuss religion and philosophy with me."

"Time will tell," said Tan Bang. He and his mother spent another hour looking at treasures from the Dynasty chest and planning a bright future for his son.

Tan Bang stayed true to his promise. He remained an honest worker even though others were stealing from their departments. Eventually they were caught and some were jailed. Tan Bang was respected for his integrity and even got a promotion. The lesson he learned from the Dynasty chest was a valuable one.

April had a coughing fit, and Josh paused, taking off the hat. "I'll get us both some water," he said, heading into the kitchen.

"The baby was funny," said April approvingly, as she sipped from her glass. "Can you tell me the next story now?"

Josh replaced the hat and began story number three.

Tan Bang's son was named Tan Cai. He didn't become a scholar as his grandmother had hoped, but she loved him anyway. He became a wealthy jewel trader and traveled all around the country. When he was fifty years old, his father died and he became the keeper of the Dynasty chest. He and his wife and children lived in a large comfortable house on the edge of town, and he kept the Dynasty chest in a special room built just for it.

One autumn, there were several burglaries in their town. Tan Cai was worried for his family and his home. He knew the burglars would target him, the jewel merchant. He decided to send his wife and children to her sister's, and he hoped the authorities would catch the burglars quickly. But Tan Cai was still worried about the safety of the Dynasty chest. How could he guard it? How could he make sure that it was safe? After he saw his family off, he spent the rest of the afternoon walking around his property, worrying and thinking.

As the Dynasty chest keeper, Tan Cai had been taught all the stories of the items in the chest, and had added his own. When he was just starting his business, his mother-in-law had given him a gift: a brass money tree with coins for leaves, about the size of a small hand. A figure of a man stood on one of the branches, onto another branch as if to shake it. The man was the mythical genie of wealth, Lu Ti. The charm was supposed to bring good luck and prosperity to whoever owned it. It was one of Tan Cai's favorite items in the Dynasty chest.

And now it gave him an idea. Several tung trees flanked the lane leading to the house. As a boy, he had enjoyed climbing trees and playing pranks on his friends by dropping ripe fruit on their heads. Tonight was not a night for pranks, though. Tan Cai climbed one of the tung trees quickly and quietly. He settled onto a branch and looked around. He had a good view of his house and the lane, and would be able to see if any burglars were approaching. But what would he do if he did see a thief? He wasn't sure. Maybe this idea was foolish. If any of his neighbors saw the wealthy jewel merchant Tan Cai in a tree, they would wonder if he was crazy.

He stood up from his sitting position on the branch, thinking he might climb down after all. As he did so, a few of the branches moved and caused the leaves on them to shimmer. It was fall, and the leaves of the tung tree had turned golden. Tan Cai could easily see how the ancients had gotten the idea for the money tree from the leaves' rounded shape and shimmering color. He felt like a boy again as he shook the branch and watched a few golden leaves fall to the ground, glinting in the setting sun. He was the genie of wealth himself! He smiled. Ah, well. If only making money was that easy. Now he was up in a tree trying to protect his hard-earned wealth from burglars.

The next minute, his thoughts were interrupted by anxious whispering voices. Three men were coming down the path toward him. "There is no movement in the house," said one. "The family is away. I've been watching this house and I saw them leave today."

"Good," said another. "We can break in easily. I'm sure he has many jewels. And who knows what other valuables there might be?"

It was the thieves, all right. They were almost right below his tree!

"Wait a minute," said the third burglar. "I'm not feeling very brave. I need more wine." The three of them stopped right under the tung tree and pulled out a wine flask. They passed it around, helping themselves to plenty of liquid courage.

Tan Cai moved nervously on the branch, almost losing his balance.

"What was that?" asked one of the burglars, looking up.

Tan Cai froze in fear. The shadows were long but it wasn't dark yet. They would see him! What should he do? A few leaves fell from the tree, golden, round and shimmering. Then an idea came to him. He cleared his throat and spoke in the deepest, most booming voice he could muster.

"Ha ha! You are fortunate indeed to have found me."

"Who are you? What are you doing up there?" the burglars shouted.

"Who else would be in a money tree? I am Lu Ti, the mythical genie of wealth!"

Tan Cai desperately hoped this ruse would fool the thieves. Before they could ask any more questions, he began to shake the branches of the tree. The golden leaves rained down.

"Do you not see the magic happening?" he said in his Lu Ti voice. "These leaves will soon change to gold coins. Let them touch the ground. Once they do, gather them carefully. Take them to the fountain in the center of town and place them in the water. After a few minutes they will sink. When you take them out of the water, they will be gold coins."

Tan Cai shook the branches again. "Do not delay!" he shouted in his most commanding tones. "Gather the leaves and hurry! The magic I have laid on them will only last for a short time!"

The burglars were speechless, but they were convinced. They hurriedly gathered the leaves as Tan Cai tried to suppress his laughter.

"Go quickly now!" he demanded once they had picked up all the leaves. "Go to the fountain. Tell no one about this magic. It is for you and you alone. Ha ha ha ha!"

The burglars ran toward the center of town, excited with their good fortune. When they were out of sight, Tan Cai climbed out of the tree and made his way, chuckling, to the police station. He would tell the police that they could find the burglars at the town fountain. They would be the fools littering the water with leaves and waiting for them to sink. After that he would go home and sleep well, knowing that the precious Dynasty chest was safe.

"Grandpa," said April, yawning. "Are there any more Dynasty chest stories about little girls like me?"

"Yes," assured Josh. "The next two stories are about girls. But if you're tired, maybe you should sleep."

"No, I'm not tired," insisted April. "Not if the stories are about girls."

"Okay," said Josh. "The first little girl, Tan Hsui Mei, is a couple of years older than you in this story. Eleven, I think. She loved all the letters and poems that people had put in the Dynasty chest. But there was a problem…" Master Storyteller Grandpa began again.

Tan Hsui Mei reached into the open Dynasty chest and picked out a paper. She took it to her father who was sitting in a chair on the other side of the room.

"Again, Daughter?" asked Tan Cai, her father. "I do not have the time to read letters to you right now. Have your brother read it to you."

"He won't, Father," said Tan Hsui Mei. "He's busy flying his kite. Please, Father. I want to read the poem Great-Grandmother made up on the day you were born. It's my favorite."

"Oh, Daughter," said her father tiredly. "I love all my children, but I sometimes wish you were a boy. Then you could read on your own."

"Why do I have to be a boy to read? Can't girls read?"

"Girls can read if they are taught, but it is not necessary for them to learn."

"I think it is necessary for me," Tan Hsui Mei said seriously. "If I am going to be the keeper of the Dynasty chest after you die, I need to know what is in it. I want to read all the letters and stories and poems. Really, Father. The Dynasty chest keeper should know how to read!"

Tan Cai looked down at his daughter's solemn face. He wanted to smile, but he didn't. She was taking her responsibility as Dynasty chest keeper very seriously, and he was proud of her.

"You are right, Daughter. The Dynasty chest keeper will learn to read."

Tan Hsui Mei learned to read quickly, and devoured every written word that was in the Dynasty chest. In fact, she read everything she could get her hands on: her brothers' schoolbooks, her father's business papers, and whatever she could borrow from anyone who was willing to lend a girl a book.

She married at the age of twenty-one. Her first child was a girl, and Tan Hsui Mei taught her to read as soon as she could get the little one to sit still. This child, Meng Kew, would be the next keeper of the Dynasty chest, and a new tradition was born. Whether the keeper was a girl or a boy, being able to read would now be part of the responsibility.

Tan Hsui Mei had a full and happy life. She liked reading and discussing books with her husband, but something was lacking in her friendship with other women. One evening after helping little Meng Kew study her letters, Tan Hsui Mei had an idea. She turned to her husband, who was finishing a cup of tea.

"I have a wonderful idea," she said excitedly.

"Tell me," said her husband with a smile. "I always like your ideas."

"I want to teach more women to read," she said. "I have friends in the village who would like their daughters to learn. And some of them long to read, too. I would like to meet here at our home once a week with any woman or girl who wishes to learn to read. I will teach them and we will discuss literature and issues of the day."

"It is a good idea," agreed her husband. "Times are changing. A woman who reads can be a great help in her family and the community."

Tan Hsui Mei began the project with a few friends and their daughters, and it quickly grew. Within a year she was hosting a dozen women and girls every week. Some people in the

seemed very sincere to her. They mostly cared about looks and money, just as her friends did. Meng Kew began to wonder if she would ever marry.

Her friends wondered the same thing. Most of them were getting married and they pressured Meng Kew to pick someone. She started to think that maybe they were right. Maybe she was being too particular. After all, many of these young men were wealthy and came from good families. Wouldn't she have a secure life married to one of them?

One afternoon, a young man came to visit. Meng Kew told her parents she had a headache and didn't want to see him. She slipped away into the family shrine room where the Dynasty chest was kept. One day she would be the keeper of the chest. The first child that she would have with her chosen husband would become the keeper of the chest after her, if she ever married. Meng Kew sat on the floor next to the chest and opened the lid. She absentmindedly began to move some items around when her hand touched a part of the chest that moved. It was the molding around the rim of the chest that hid the secret side compartment!

A secret compartment? Did anyone else know this was here? She couldn't believe what she had found! She lifted off the covering. Her hand was just small enough to reach down to the bottom, and she lifted out a small thin box. It was a red lacquered box with a dragon carved on the lid.

Who built the secret compartment? Who put this box here? Meng Kew wondered as she carefully opened the box. Inside was a single beautiful pearl nestled in silk. She lifted the pearl and held it in her palm.

A pearl is a symbol of chasing after wisdom, thought Meng Kew. And I certainly need some wisdom now. She thought about her life and what she wanted in the future. She didn't need to marry a rich man to be able to live well, since she would bring a good dowry to her marriage. So what should she look for in a husband? What was more valuable than money?

The answer came as she held the pearl up to the warm afternoon light coming from the window. Happiness was worth more than wealth and social standing, she decided. Meng Kew thoughtfully rolled the pearl in her hand. What did she need in her life? What was she chasing after? Her mother always told her that wisdom brings happiness, and that was the answer. That's what she wanted: happiness. Meng Kew knew that she would not be happy with any of the suitors who had pursued her so far. She did not know how she would find him, but she knew that she wanted to find a husband she could be happy with. That was the most important thing.

Meng Kew felt as if a weight had been lifted off her shoulders as she took one last look at the pearl, put it in the box and slid it back into the secret compartment. She couldn't wait to tell her mother what she had found in the Dynasty chest.

Satisfied with her new goal, Meng Kew stopped worrying about who she was going to marry. Her friends gave up playing matchmaker, and the young men of the town stopped coming around. But after a few months she met the man of her choice. He was a young farmer who brought his fruits and vegetables into town to sell. Meng Kew had talked to him once when she went into town to buy mangoes. After that first meeting, she found reasons to go into town almost every day, and by the end of the year, the relationship turned into love. Her parents were a little surprised that she wanted to marry a farmer, but Meng Kew knew her own mind and they trusted her choice.

Meng Kew didn't marry into money or prestige. She didn't know what the future would bring, but she knew that she and her husband would make a wonderful life together no matter what the future held. It was indeed a happy wedding. At the feast, the bride and groom drank a toast from a cup made out of a rhino horn, which symbolizes happiness.

It would be many years before she took possession of the Dynasty chest, but after her wedding, she asked her mother for permission to put an object in it. The rhino horn cup went into the chest as a symbol of Meng Kew's wish for happiness, now and in the future.

Josh felt a bit of a leg cramp. He stood and stretched, then walked to the window. He smiled, noticing a brown sparrow on a tree branch. "There's one more story I remember from Gramps' journal, Blossom," said Josh. "But it's about a boy. Do you want to hear it?"

"Sure," said April. "Boys are okay sometimes. What else is in the story?"

"Birds. Lots of birds."

"Do they hunt the birds?" asked April, suspiciously. She was a pacifist.

"Nope. No birds were harmed in the making of this story," answered Josh.

"Okay, then. Go ahead."

Josh sat back on the bed and began story number six.

Liu Peng was this boy's name, and he was the only child of Meng Kew. He was a sickly baby and his parents worried that he might die. Would he live to adulthood, long enough to be the Dynasty chest keeper? They focused all their energies on taking care of him, and he did survive. The celebration on his first birthday was very happy. But as he got older, Liu Peng was still weak and small for his age. He was teased by the other children a lot, so he spent most of his time indoors.

When Liu Peng became bored with his books and other indoor activities, he would sometimes go outside to take a walk. His mother hoped the fresh air would make him healthier. The walks were good for him, helping to strengthen his legs and lungs. Sometimes he walked with his friends, but most of the time he was alone, because he could walk at his own pace and rest when he needed to.

When he sat on a stone or a tree stump to rest, he liked to watch the birds, especially the pigeons. There was an elderly neighbor who had a prize flock of pigeons. When Liu Peng was ten years old, he walked more and more often to the neighbor's house to watch him work with the pigeons.

The old gentleman was impressed with the respectful, quiet young boy. He let him help with the pigeons, and within a year Liu Peng had become proficient at handling the birds. The old pigeon keeper taught Liu Peng everything he knew. He gave the boy a pair of pigeons as a gift which Liu Peng trained himself. Since he was not able to play sports or enjoy active games, his parents were happy to see that he had an activity he was interested in. Liu Peng grew stronger as he spent more and more time outdoors tending the birds.

Liu Peng accompanied the old gentleman to town to show his pigeons in competition. One part of the competition was to attach whistles to a pigeon's tail and send it flying. The air moving through the whistles made pretty music. The pigeons who flew the longest and highest and made the most pleasing music received prizes. When Liu Peng was fifteen, the old gentleman retired from pigeon competition. He gave Liu Peng his birds and equipment, and came to the competitions to cheer for him. Liu Peng was grateful to the old man for all the learning he had received from him.

Liu Peng's pigeons did well in the flight competitions but were never the best at making music. Some birders used clay whistles; some were made from gourds, and some from bamboo. Liu Peng used bamboo whistles on his birds because they were the lightest. He tried different shapes and sizes but never won first place for his birds' music. One day, he decided to ask the winner of the music competition about his whistles.

"Respectfully, sir," he said with a bow as he approached the man. "Congratulations on your victory today."

"And on yours," answered the man. "Your gray pigeon flew the highest."

"But yours make the most beautiful music," said Liu Peng. "Can I ask who supplies your whistles?"

"It is no secret," said the man cordially. "Look next to the tea stand. The young woman there makes the whistles for my birds and for a few others. Come, I will introduce you."

"Hello, Huang Linqin!" called the man as they walked over. A slight girl with long fingers looked up from the table where she sat working on a piece of bamboo.

"This is Liu Peng," said the man. "He competes with a fine flock of pigeons here. Now if you will excuse me, I must go tend to my birds."

"Hello," said Huang Linqin to Liu Peng. "I have seen your birds. They are very beautiful, and fast, too."

"Thank you. I have been working with pigeons since I was a young boy. How long have you been making bamboo pigeon whistles?" Liu Peng asked.

"A few years," she answered. "My mother and grandmother made the whistles before me. My mother taught me how before she died."

"I am sorry for the loss of your mother," responded Liu Peng sincerely. "But she and your grandmother taught you well. Your whistles make the most beautiful music of them all."

"Do you think so?" asked Huang Linqin. "They are not the most elaborate. The design is really very simple." Huang Linqin held up the whistle she had just finished and handed it to Liu Peng.

"Perhaps that is what makes the music so beautiful," said Liu Peng as he turned the whistle over in his hand. "I would like to buy some whistles from you to use on my birds."

"The one you are holding is the only one I have that is not spoken for," said Huang Linqin. "You may take it. Try it on one of your birds, and if you like it you can pay me for it later, and order more."

"I am sure I will want to order more. Thank you." Liu Peng bowed. "I will let you know how my pigeons like the whistle."

The whistle made the most pleasing sound Liu Peng had ever heard from his birds, and he went back to order more whistles from Huang Linqin the next day. Although he was shy, another reason he went back was just to be with her. She was so quiet and gentle and graceful. He loved to sit at her table and watch her nimble fingers carve and shape the bamboo whistles that would be attached to a pigeon's tail to make beautiful music. He started to spend as much time with Huang Linqin as he did with his birds. She enjoyed being with Liu Peng, too. He was thoughtful, intelligent and polite; not arrogant and rude like some of the young men.

It soon became apparent to everyone who came to watch the birds that these young people were a match. The quiet boy who kept birds and the gentle girl who made music for the birds became husband and wife. They were devoted to each other and kept beautiful flocks of pigeons all their lives.

When Liu Peng inherited the Dynasty chest from his mother and became the keeper, the first thing he placed in it was that bamboo pigeon whistle Huang Linqin had given him on the day they met. It was a reminder of their past and how they had come together. It was still a part of their present, and it helped them see into the future: a future of beauty, music and togetherness.

"Blossom?" asked Josh. His granddaughter's eyes were closed. "Are you awake?"

"Uh-huh," answered April, her eyes still shut. "I'm imagining what it would be like to watch a pigeon flying around with a whistle on its tail. Can I have a pigeon, Grandpa?" she asked, opening her eyes and sitting up.

"People around here don't keep pigeons," said Josh. "But we can fly a kite and put a whistle on it like the Chinese kids do. As soon as you're up and around again, we'll build a kite together. Now you better get some sleep. That's all the stories I remember." He took off the pirate hat and tossed it into the toy box.

"Okay. Thanks for the stories, Grandpa." April yawned as Josh tucked her in for a nap. She was already halfway to dreamland, which would be filled with stories from the Dynasty chest.

— Chapter 3 —

The Dynasty Chest Creates a Wise Man

Josh didn't recall any more stories of the Dynasty chest keepers the day he visited his sneezing granddaughter. Six stories were enough for one session anyway, and April needed to sleep. But the Dynasty chest and its legacy moved on after Liu Peng, the boy who kept pigeons. Liu Peng and his wife had a baby in 1513. The child's name was Liu Shen, and he followed his grandfather in the business of farming and selling produce in the hills outside Beijing. He grew into a strong, competent farmer and married, but became a widower several years later. Liu Shen's first wife had died with no children. He married again, and desperately longed for children with his young second wife. However, years went by with no pregnancy. Liu Shen would eventually have to pass on the Dynasty chest. Without a son or daughter to take on the responsibility, what would happen to it?

Now it was 1573. Liu Shen was in his family shrine room, pacing nervously. He held a charm in his hand that he had taken from the Dynasty chest. It was in the shape of a gourd, and would help in warding off evil. His second wife was giving birth, and he would finally have a child! His grip tightened on the gourd charm as he paced. Would a son or a daughter be born? It did not matter, as long as there was a child to guard the treasures in the Dynasty chest.

Liu Shen stopped to open the Dynasty chest again. He touched the peacock feather that he had placed there months ago, remembering. He and his wife had seen a peacock as they were walking on the outskirts of the village. His wife stopped in her tracks. "Husband," she said in a hushed voice. "Legend has it that one glance from a peacock can make a woman pregnant. Stand still!" Sure enough, the peacock turned and looked her straight in the eye, and in the same month she was with child. Liu Shen smiled to himself, recalling how happy his wife had been when she told him that he would be a father.

The women who were attending to Liu Shen's wife broke his reverie with good news. His wife was doing well, and he had a son, born in the year of the rooster. He smiled in happiness and relief. He was sixty years old and finally had a son!

Liu Li Yong was a beloved child, but his boyhood years were lonely. He grew up working alongside his father on the farm, but had no siblings. Like most rural children, he did not go to school. He was often alone, and occupied himself by looking at the treasures in the Dynasty chest. He would pick up one of the objects and try to imagine the life of the person who had owned it. It was an odd and quiet pastime for a young boy, but it caused his imagination and sense of wonder to grow.

His father made sure that Liu Li Yong understood that he was destined to be the keeper of the Dynasty chest. As the boy grew older, Liu Shen made a ritual of showing his son items from the chest, telling him their stories and explaining their lessons. They passed many hours together this way, especially as Liu Shen grew older and feebler.

Although he was the son of a farmer, Liu Li Yong didn't particularly enjoy farming. He liked to work with his hands, but had little skill with crops and was not intuitive with animals. By the time he was sixteen years old, the farm was failing. He had to find a way to support his parents, for his father was now seventy-six years old.

Liu Li Yong asked his father for advice one evening as they were looking through the Dynasty chest. These evenings had developed into a comfortable pattern. Liu Shen would take an item out of the Dynasty chest, show it to his son, set it on the table before them and talk about it. He told Liu Li Yong how old it was, which of their ancestors had placed it in the chest, and why it was important. This particular evening, before his father opened the chest, Liu Li Yong told him of his worries.

"Father, you were a good farmer and I have tried to work with the land as you did. But our crops have been failing for several years now. I am afraid it is because of my lack of skill as a farmer. I want to support you and Mother as you age, but I fear the farm will not sustain us much longer. Father, what should my course of action be? Should I continue to try to work the farm?"

Liu Shen listened to his son, nodding now and then. He opened the Dynasty chest and took out a bronze tree about the size of a child's hand. "My son," he said. "You do honor to your parents with your concern. Now let me tell you a story that this tree reminds me of. It was put into the Dynasty chest by our ancestor Tan Cai." He settled back onto his cushion and began, holding the tree.

"An old man gave a farmer a special seed. He told the farmer to plant the seed, water it every day, and it would sprout. But the water had to be beads of sweat from the farmer himself. Once the seed had sprouted, it would need more water. But then the water had to be drops of the farmer's blood. The farmer did as he was instructed. Using his own sweat and blood from hard work, he made the seed sprout and grow. When it matured, the plant grew to be a money tree. The farmer found that when he shook the tree, coins fell to the ground and the tree became a source of perpetual wealth."

Liu Shen handed the bronze money tree to Liu Li Yong. "You see, son," he said "Whatever work you decide to do, success and riches are achieved through honest effort and hard work. You are not entirely to blame for the farm failing. The storms in recent years have gotten worse. They say it is because the Emperor no longer has the mandate of heaven. Many changes are coming. You may change along with the times, my son.

Here is my advice. There is a man in the village, a bricklayer, who has no sons. He is looking for an apprentice. I can send you to him to learn his craft."

Liu Li Yong smiled as he handed the bronze tree charm back to his father. "Thank you, Father, for the lesson of the money tree. I will work hard. I will do my best with my own sweat and blood to create prosperity so that I can provide for you and Mother in your old age."

Liu Shen placed the money tree back in the Dynasty chest and closed the lid. "Remember, my son, you will be the keeper of the Dynasty chest when I die. You are responsible for the treasures it contains and the legacies it holds."

Liu Li Yong took his responsibilities seriously, growing from a quiet, contemplative youngster to a skilled and confident young man. He began to learn bricklaying from his mentor in the village. He was eighteen years old, only two years into his apprenticeship, when his father died in 1591. He traveled home to the farm to comfort his mother and to take possession of the Dynasty chest. He housed his mother in the village while he worked the last three years of his apprenticeship. When it was completed, his mentor told him that bricklayers were needed in the city of Beijing to help fortify and repair the Great Wall.

Liu Li Yong always thought things through carefully before he made a decision. He was still as soft-spoken and contemplative as he was in his youth, but he had gained confidence and strength of character over the years. He told his mother about the opportunity in Beijing and she agreed to go. They traveled to the city, and Liu Li Yong soon found work reinforcing the Great Wall.

The young man created a special place in his new home for the Dynasty chest. It sat on a wooden platform and was covered by a red silk cloth. As was his habit all his life, he spent many an hour reflecting on the precious artifacts in the chest. His ancestors had left an astounding legacy. Ancient charms, beautiful lacquered boxes, and precious pieces of jewelry passed through Liu Li Yong's hands. He shined the blade of Marco Polo's jeweled dagger and marveled at the intricacy of his ancient compass. There were more recent treasures, too. Liu Li Yong chuckled to himself as he discovered a bamboo dragonfly spinner that he had played with as a child. He thought of his own children playing with the toy and tossing it back and forth to each other; something he could not do as an only child. Playing alone was a lonely endeavor. He wanted children—a child to become the Dynasty chest keeper, certainly, but other children too. Brothers and sisters to share the laughter and joy that he had missed.

Liu Li Yong sighed and sat back as he closed the Dynasty chest with the dragonfly toy inside it. He had been in Beijing for five years. He had no children yet. He had no wife yet. Well, it was time to change that, he thought. Prosperity and happiness don't come without effort. And it would take some effort for this shy young man to start a family of his own. "Mother!" he called, with a bit of a catch in his voice. "Let us speak to the matchmaker."

They began the process, and the matchmaker was successful in finding Liu Li Yong a young, good-natured bride. She came to live with her new husband and mother-in-law and brought the household much joy, but no children. After Liu Li Yong's mother died, he thought more and about his legacy. The years passed, and he found himself married fifteen years without children. What would the future of the Dynasty chest be?

Liu Li Yong was still in the habit of opening the Dynasty chest in the evenings and looking at the artifacts. His wife sat with him one night and they noticed the peacock feather that his father had placed in it the day he was born. Liu Li Yong knew the story well, and had an idea.

"My wife, hold the peacock feather up and look right in its eye," he urged. She gave him a questioning look but did as he asked.

"This isn't the same as catching the glance of an actual peacock," she said to him. "But I will do as you say to keep your good humor. You know I desire children as much as you do."

She smiled, held the peacock feather up as if looking into a mirror and stared into its eye. As she did so, Liu Li Yong gazed at his wife, admiring her gentle beauty. She was still a fairly young woman, but her time for childbearing would soon be past. Children or not, he would love and care for her till the end of their days.

"Come, wife. If the peacock feather has worked any magic, it must have taken effect by now. Let us retire for the night." She smiled, stood and took his hand, and led him into the bedchamber.

The peacock feather did work its magic. Or was it the magic of the Dynasty chest? A son was born to the couple the next year, in 1616 and another two years later. The boys grew up in a happy, noisy, loving household. The older boy, Liu Li Jun, was fascinated with weapons and fighting. He loved to watch the troops of soldiers that often passed by on the road to Beijing. He spent his young days playing with toy sabers and bows, eventually learning swordsmanship and archery.

Liu Zhang Wei, the younger son, played soldier with his brother but got bored watching troops march past the house. Sometimes, though, elephants were brought into the city and were driven down the same road. He could sit all day and watch the elephants lumber by. Once, a line of elephants stopped and an elephant keeper came to their door asking for water for one of his men who was ill. The group rested for a few hours and Liu Zhang Wei talked to the elephant keeper. He allowed the boy to pet a baby elephant and showed him the commands the elephants were taught. These animals were being taken to the Forbidden City where the emperor lived, the keeper said. He described its beautiful buildings and gardens. It sounded like heaven to Liu Zhang Wei.

Liu Li Yong became a master bricklayer in the year 1638 and began to teach apprentices of his own. He often traveled to various sections of the Great Wall around Beijing, inspecting the wall and supervising repairs. The Wall, with the rebuilding and repairs almost completed, had become the symbol of the Ming Dynasty's power and grandeur.

The older son, Liu Li Jun, became quite proficient as a bowman and wanted to join the Army. His father gave him his blessing. Before his son left, however, Liu Li Yong reminded him that he was the keeper of the Dynasty chest.

"Use the Dynasty chest, my son," he said. "It will enable you to tap into the wisdom of reflection. I spent many hours contemplating the items in the Dynasty chest and the wisdom and the legacy they impart. Meditation and reflection are necessary in the pursuit of wisdom. They are necessary for a happy and balanced life, especially a life like yours, which will be full of danger and adventure. I am pleased with your decision to join the army, but I want you to be able to reflect on the goodness of life and the goodness of your fellow man as well. People are trustworthy if you honor them with trust. It does not hurt you to trust everyone. It is a good place from which to start relationships."

"I will take the responsibility of the Dynasty chest to heart, Father," the young man assured him. The wife and younger son entered with tea. "Ah, here is Mother and Younger Brother."

After refreshing himself with the hot drink, Liu Li Yong spoke again. "After you leave for Beijing, my son, I must follow soon. I have an inspection tour of the wall that is overdue. Younger Brother, you will stay here and look after Mother until I return. She has not been well lately. Pay close attention to her health and wait on her well. I depend on you to take care of her until I return." He held his wife's hand and smiled on his sons, hoping for the best for both of them.

impressed with it. It took a million men and countless hours to form the bricks and mix the mortar, to haul the materials up the steep slopes, to lay the foundations, and place the bricks. Men from the lower classes were drafted by the tens of thousands for this work. They were forced to leave their homes and families and spend months, even years, in the service of the Emperor. Farmers were taken from their fields, workers from their villages, and even convicts were brought out from the prisons, because so many hands were needed.

Many people were resentful of this conscription, not only because they had to leave their towns and families, but because the work was backbreaking. The construction never stopped, and whether the temperature was extremely hot or extremely cold, the men worked on. Because of injury and illness, many workers died. This was the cruelest fate of all, because as they were far from family and home, there was no way to give them proper burials. Their bodies were tossed into the interior of the wall that was also filled with debris, stones and earth. The wall may have been a great accomplishment for the Ming emperors, but for the common people of China, it personified suffering, loss and death.

Building and rebuilding the Great Wall

Liu Li Yong was aware of the unhappiness among the workers at the wall. He did his best to persuade his superiors and the soldiers supervising the work to treat their men humanely. As he made his way to the wall at Simatai to inspect the bricklayers' work, he prayed to find the men healthy and in good spirits.

The wall at Simatai was a three mile section of very steep terrain. It was dangerous work. To Liu Li Yong's relief, the weather was mild and the work seemed to be progressing well. He was pleased with the craftsmanship of the bricklayers, and spent a few days at the wall monitoring the construction of the bricks and their transfer by goats to one of the many watchtowers being constructed. The watchtowers would be manned by soldiers day and night, ready to defend the city of Beijing and the Emperor in the Forbidden City.

Liu Li Yong was inspecting a kiln one afternoon when he heard a familiar voice behind him. "Sir?" the voice said.

He turned and saw his oldest son, proudly arrayed in uniform.

"Father!" the young man exclaimed. "It is you. I wondered when I was assigned to Simatai if I would see you. I have been assigned the rank of captain. These are my men reinforcing this section of the wall." He gestured toward the men working at the base of the wall, and the look on his face became one of worry. His voice became quiet and urgent.

"Father, I am glad you are here. I must ask your advice."

"Then you must call me *Míngzhì Sou*, as the workers here do," said his father with a smile. The old man arranged to meet with his son in his tent that evening. As they drank a pot of tea together, Liu Li Jun explained to his father what he needed.

"The men of my regiment are good men. They work hard. We have been here less than a week, so they are still fresh. But I worry about their health and their state of mind. Many of them do not want to be here. The work is very hard and dangerous on these steep hills, and they don't consider it soldier's work. What can I do to keep their spirits up?"

old man looked around the room. The space on the wooden platform underneath the Dynasty chest was dusty. As long as the chest was empty, he would move it, clean the platform, replace the chest, and put the items back in.

He gave out a surprised grunt as he attempted to lift the chest. Yes, he was an old man, but he was still healthy enough to lift an empty wooden chest. What was wrong? He tried lifting one end, then the other. The bottom of the chest was incredibly heavy. He looked inside the chest and removed a silk cloth that was still lying at the bottom. The wood he exposed looked different than the rest of the chest. This gave the wise old man an idea. He measured the depth inside the chest, and then measured the height of the outside. The measurement on the inside was one inch shorter than the measurement on the outside. He had his answer. The chest had a false bottom.

It didn't take much effort to remove it. He slid a file in between the false bottom and the side of the chest until the false bottom popped out in one piece. He lifted it out of the chest and was amazed by what he saw underneath.

The gold coins that had not seen the light of day since the time of Marco Polo and his Sherpa guide lay in the bottom of the chest, protected individually by leather wrappings. The old man lifted them out and unwrapped them, one by one. Fifty solid gold coins, beautifully worked with the emblem of the ancient Kublai Khan stamped on each one. Of all the amazing items in the Dynasty chest, this was a treasure beyond belief. The old man sat, stunned, for several minutes.

It was fortunate for the keepers of the Dynasty chest that Liu Li Yong was so wise. A lesser man might have wasted this treasure or even let it destroy his life. The old man had no such temptation. He was quiet, wise and deliberate in everything he did. He sat thoughtfully, looking at the glint of the gold coins in the afternoon sunlight, filtered softly through the paper window. He weighed his options.

I have enough money to keep my wife comfortable after I die, he thought. My older son has a good position with the army. My younger son does not possess the maturity to handle such wealth. I will leave the inventory sheet as it is, without adding the coins to it, he decided with finality. "They were hidden once and will be hidden again," he said softly as he stood. Liu Li Yong found another box to hold the coins temporarily. He replaced the false bottom in the empty chest, which now moved easily. He dusted the platform and put the chest back in its place. Then he carefully and lovingly replaced all the artifacts and closed the lid. As he was smoothing the red silk on top of the chest he heard his wife call.

"Husband! Our younger son is here. He has been escorted home by the authorities."

The old man slid the box now containing the coins under the wooden platform and went outside to meet his son. The officer spoke firmly.

"Your son was with a group of young men who were caught with stolen goods last night. He did not have any goods on him, but if he is found in the company of these others again or is found with stolen goods, he will go directly to prison."

The old man bowed to the officer and thanked him for his trouble. After he left, the family silently went inside their home. They drank tea while Liu Li Yong talked to the young man.

"My son, I do not have to give you a lecture about what is right and what is wrong. You learned these things at a young age. You must take responsibility for your own path in life. I hope that you will change your path to a trustworthy and honorable one. Remember, every knot can be undone, no matter how tight it may appear."

The young man dropped his head in shame. "I will try, Father. I am sorry that you are disappointed in me."

Liu Li Yong was reassured, but was not through with his son. "One more thing," the old man said. "I took an inventory of the items in the Dynasty chest today. Did you forget to replace the money tree after the last time you took it out of the chest?"

"Yes, Father. Here it is," said Liu Zhang Wei as he took the bronze tree from his pocket and handed it to the old man.

"No. Keep it with you. As you plan your future life and profession it will remind you of the rewards of hard work." The old man wanted his son to know that he trusted him to do the right thing. He wanted him to learn the wisdom of the money tree.

"As you wish, Father." The son replaced the charm in his pocket. He wondered how much money he could get for its sale.

"I must make another trip to the Great Wall at Simatai in a few days," the old man said as he prepared to leave the room. "I trust, my son, that you will learn from this mistake and conduct yourself in a more honorable manner."

"Yes, Father," the young man said, bowing as he opened the door for his father.

Liu Li Yong's trip to Simatai was not one that had been planned. This was to be a personal trip, but he let everyone believe that another inspection had been scheduled. He set off early the next week with a horse and cart containing provisions. The cart also contained the box with the fifty gold coins. The old man had taken the leather-wrapped coins and placed five each in ten drawstring leather bags. Back in the box, they were hidden under a bag of rice and a tin of tea.

His older son was happy to see him again at Simatai a few mornings later. Liu Li Jun was managing his troops well and the old man saw that many regiments had added bricks to the wall with their code numbers stamped on them.

After sleeping during the hottest part of the day, the old man emerged from his tent with a piece of tanned leather and pen and ink concealed in a deep pocket of his robe. He made a show of inspecting the kilns and a recently completed watch tower. He took reports from his son and a few of the other captains until work was done for the day. The soldiers went to the evening meal, but the old man stayed behind at the wall. He inspected the section of the wall where the renovation work had ended for the day. Past that section there was crumbling earth, loose stones, and broken brickwork. The next day it would be covered by new bricks and mortar.

The old man creates the map

He looked closely at the wall and smiled. The brickwork really was fine, he thought, as he ran his fingers along the bricks stamped with the code numbers of the different army regiments. These numbers would help him find the coins again when it was time to reveal them to his sons.

Liu Li Yong sat down in front of the wall with the leather, his pen and ink, and proceeded to create a map that showed the exact point where he would bury the coins in the Great Wall of China. On the map, he described the coins, and the leather bags. He chose a brick stamped with his son's regiment number that was at the edge of the renovated part of the wall. He recorded the number of that brick, and estimated where the new bricks would be placed to the right of it. The new bricks were six inches long. He counted seven six-inch spaces up from the stamped brick, and then seven six-inch spaces to the right. He dabbed a blot of ink on a stone. This spot, on the old part of the wall, is where he would bury the coins. Tomorrow the spot would be laid over with new bricks, and his treasure would be safe. After he had written the clues on the map, he rolled it up and stood, stretching his tired limbs in the dimming light before walking back to his tent to rest. It would need to be fully dark before he completed the job.

Later that night he left his tent, carrying the box and a small shovel. No one saw him. He walked back to the section of the wall that he had chosen earlier. It was easy to loosen the earth and move a few stones and remnants of brick with the shovel. With little trouble, the old man created a hole in the wall. He dug several feet in and then turned to the box at his feet. Inside were the ten precious bags of coins. Opening the box, he removed the heavy bags one by one and placed them as far back in the hole as he could. Using the shovel, he filled the space in again with dirt and replaced a few stones and old bricks. Tomorrow the workers would build a new layer of bricks in front of this old crumbling wall.

The coins are hidden inside the wall

Satisfied that the coins would be well hidden, the old man took the empty box and walked in the silence of the night back to his tent. The only witnesses to his secret were the spirits of the men who had died building the wall and were now buried in it.

The leather map, rolled up and tied with a leather cord, was the last and most important thing Liu Li Yong added to the Dynasty chest. He hid it under the false bottom where the coins had rested secretly for so many years. The old man didn't know it then, but this trek to Simatai to hide the coins would be his last trip to the wall. His health began to fail and he was compelled to retire.

The younger brother was still at home. He had not married, nor found work. He helped his mother take care of his elderly father but was still possessed by a spirit of discontent. The money tree burned in his pocket. He knew the story of how blood and sweat was necessary to achieve prosperity, but he wouldn't accept it. He wished there was some way to get around it.

Sometimes he wandered into the room where the Dynasty chest was kept. He looked through a few of the things and always ended up taking out the bamboo dragonfly spinner that he and his brother had played with as children. They had spent many sunny afternoons spinning it back and forth to each other, while their father happily watched. He was sad as he replaced the toy in the chest. Childhood was gone, and he had no idea how to move on.

Liu Li Jun had taken a leave from the army to visit his aging father. The morning after he arrived, he took his younger brother aside while their parents were still asleep. Pulling Liu Zhang Wei roughly by the arm, his brother led him outside to the shade of a plum tree and began to scold.

"My brother! You dishonor our parents and our ancestors. You're old enough to learn a trade and earn your keep. Stop being lazy. Stop associating with those friends of yours in the village who were arrested for theft."

The young man did not respond. Liu Li Jun shook his arm and tried to look him in the eye. "What is wrong with you? When mother is well again, enlist. Join me in the army. Father will be proud of you, and you will have some pride in yourself."

Liu Zhang Wei pulled away from his brother's grasp and walked across the garden. How could he say what he was thinking? He was fearful—afraid of failing, afraid of going into the army, afraid of disappointing his parents. His older brother was strong, confident and successful. He was none of those things, and didn't think he ever would be.

"I will find a way to make our father proud of me," he said. "But I will not join the army. The men in your regiment are little more than slaves. They do nothing but work on that wretched wall."

His brother's voice rose in frustration. "You are only fooling yourself! I know you have no plans. I know you have no training. You may be called upon as a civilian to work on the wall. At least you'll be treated better as a soldier. Listen to me, brother!"

His words fell on deaf ears as Liu Zhang Wei stormed back into the house. But the old man had heard every word, and it worried him greatly. What would happen if he told his sons about the gold coins he had found in the Dynasty chest? They were already fighting. They were not behaving like brothers. What would happen if they had this great treasure to fight over? No, he would wait. He would tell them about the coins and the map later. Maybe when Liu Li Jun was ready to return to his regiment, his sons would treat each other as brothers again.

In a few weeks, the mother's illness returned. She died peacefully in bed with her husband and sons by her side. Liu Li Yong was filled with sadness. He was tired and old, and his wife was gone. He was content to die soon himself.

But he still held the secret of the coins. He struggled with what to tell his sons. He wanted them to benefit from the riches the coins would bring, but he was afraid of the effect it might have on them.

Time was running out, however. Liu Li Yong called out to his sons one afternoon as he was lying on his couch. It was now or never. The old man's breath was shallow, his limbs were weak, and his mind was starting to cloud. Before he died he had to tell his sons the secret. He could hear them in the garden, arguing again, unable to hear his frail voice. His older son was upbraiding his younger for not properly cooking the rice. Their voices drifted in.

"I am not your wife! You have no right to talk to me like this."

"I would never marry a wife who was as lazy and irresponsible as you. You dishonor the idea." "Dishonor! Dishonor! That's all I hear you say. If I had a saber I could show you honor!"

"Ha! Your empty threats are amusing. I am going indoors to check on our father. "

As he entered the house, Liu Li Jun heard his father move restlessly on his couch and call feebly, "My son, come into my chamber. Bring Younger Brother with you. It is important."

His father's weakness worried Liu Li Jun. "Younger Brother," he called, trying to set his anger aside. "Please come into Father's chamber. He is asking for us."

Liu Zhang Wei heard the seriousness in his brother's voice. He hurried to join him at their father's bedside.

"Honored Father," began Liu Li Jun. "We are both here. What is it you wish?"

"I will die soon," said the old man. "This will be my last conversation with you. Listen well. I worked for many years supervising the building of the Great Wall. My eldest son, you also helped build the wall and took charge of many of the workers."

The old man coughed and stopped speaking to rest for a moment. Liu Li Jun spoke up. "Father, you have gained much honor and respect because of your wisdom and your skill as a bricklayer and supervisor. I have tried to live up to that ideal as your son." He looked at his brother, anger rising in him again. "I apologize for the weakness and irresponsibility of my younger brother. If it's him you are worried about, I promise you that I will take him back to the city with me and make sure he enlists in the army."

The younger man sputtered a reply. "No! I'll make my own way in life! I've no plans to join the army. You're just saying this to make yourself look good in front of our father."

"Our father is dying, and you insist on arguing? Do as you're told by your elders and be quiet." It took all of the old man's effort to interrupt his sons' bickering and speak up. He raised his hand. "Please, my sons. You must not—" He coughed in pain.

"Father, I am sorry," said Liu Zhang Wei, with a stinging looked toward his brother. Both the young men were silent as their father struggled to speak. He was growing weaker by the minute and was desperate to tell his sons the secret.

"At the wall—in the—the wall—is a treasure. Look in the chest. The Dynasty—it contains—" He coughed again.

"What, Father? It contains what?" asked Liu Li Jun.

"Don't interrupt him!" snapped his brother. "Yes, Father?"

"The chest—*Bǎo*—a treasure—*Tú*—." He struggled for words. His senses were leaving him. What was it? A map? A chart? Yes, a chart! "*Tú. Tú,*" he wheezed.

"*Wú*? No? No what? No trouble from you, I guess he means," said Liu Li Jun. "Stay away from the Dynasty chest. It's my responsibility."

"He's not talking about that!" chided his brother. "Father? Father?"

The young men knelt on either side of the couch and held their father's hands.

"My sons. Remember—you are brothers. Liu Li Jun, help your brother find—his way."

The young soldier was chastened by his father's words. "Yes, Honored Father," he said quietly. "Chest—the wall—*Tú*—*Tú*—" The old man sighed once more, closed his eyes and let out his last breath. The secret stayed with him, and the treasure remained secure in the Great Wall.

— Chapter 5 —

The Sons of Liu Li Yong:

The Dynasty Chest is an Undeserved Legacy

The death of the old man softened his sons' attitudes, at least for a short time. They visited the temple, performed the mourning rituals together and grieved for both their parents. When it was time for Liu Li Jun to return to his regiment, he spoke carefully to his younger brother.

"*Didi* (younger brother), will you follow me to Beijing? I can help you get assigned to a fine regiment."

The younger man did not know what to say. He wanted to honor his parents with good decisions, but he had no plans for a career. He only knew that he was determined to avoid the Army. "I will remain here until the mourning period is officially over. It will smooth our father's path into heaven. Then I will go to Beijing."

Liu Li Jun eyed his brother with suspicion, but did not voice it. "Bring the Dynasty chest when you come. I will be expecting you within a month."

Liu Li Jun left for Beijing and Liu Zhang Wei was alone. He felt more directionless than ever. Resuming his old habits, he wandered into the village in the evenings and took up with his old acquaintances. It wasn't long before he was joining them in vandalism and petty theft.

Several weeks passed, and Liu Li Jun became worried about his brother. It was no surprise that he had lied about coming to

Beijing, but where was he and what was he doing? The answer came on a cold, cloudy morning. As Liu Li Jun watched his regiment haul bricks up to a steep hill, he saw a line of convicts approaching. Men who had been jailed were often used as cheap labor on the Great Wall. The young officer watched as the prisoners shuffled by in single file. His heart sank when he recognized a thin young man with gangly limbs and unkempt hair. It was his brother.

"Halt!" he shouted to the soldier at the head of the line. The prisoners stopped. He made his way to where his brother was standing, wrists in shackles, eyes downcast. "*Shǎ, Shǎ Shàonián!* (Foolish, foolish youngster!)," he hissed. "So I was right. You did end up as a worker on the wall, but not as a soldier or a civilian. You are here under the worst possible circumstances: a convict. This is how you honor our parents?" Suddenly another thought occurred to him. He grabbed Liu Zhang Wei by the arm and pulled him out of the line. "Where is the Dynasty chest?" he asked worriedly. "What did you do with it? Is it safe?"

"Yes, it is safe," answered Lu Zhang Wei, still not daring to look in his brother's eyes. "Before I was taken to prison, the officers allowed me to speak with an old friend of our father's. He promised to keep watch over the house and the Dynasty chest."

"At least you did one honorable thing," said Liu Li Jun bitterly. He pushed his brother back into the line and stepped back. "Move on!" he called, with a dismissive wave of his arm.

Liu Zhang Wei said nothing more. What could he say? His brother was right. He had been caught breaking into a shop in the village, jailed, and was now forced to work on the wall as the lowest of the low. He had dishonored his parents and abandoned the Dynasty chest. His life was worth no more than the goats that carried bricks up the rocky cliffs. Liu Zhang Wei walked slowly with the other convicts toward their quarters. Much hard labor was in store for them.

The year was 1644. The Ming Dynasty was rife with corruption and excess. It was ready to fall. There were battles and skirmishes throughout China, with many ethnic groups determined to take control. Li Zicheng, from the Shaanxi province, headed a strong rebel army that had won several battles and now threatened the Great Wall at Beijing, where Li Liu Jun was stationed and where his brother had been brought to work. The troops at the Great Wall had been able to keep Li Zicheng's peasant rebels at bay, but the Ming army was being stretched thin. The Manchu also wanted control of China, and troops had to be sent to the northern border to fight the Manchu forces. While the soldiers fought, work continued on the Great Wall, mostly done by civilians and convicts.

The two brothers did not see each other again for a time. Liu Li Jun was in charge of a newly constructed watchtower. Liu Zhang Wei, since he was fairly sure-footed, had been assigned the task of hauling bricks to the top of the wall on the sections where the terrain was steepest. Yes, he thought to himself every day as he trudged up the cliffs, I am a goat.

Tension and fatigue were high among everyone. The workers at the wall were forced to build for many hours and were given little time for eating or sleeping. Scouts were sent out to determine Li Zicheng's movements, and the worried soldiers kept a constant eye on the horizon, looking and listening for signs of the approaching enemy.

On one of his routine daily trips to the top of the watchtower, Liu Li Jun saw a lone figure on horseback gallop into view. A scout was returning. He quickly went to the bottom of the tower to meet the scout. "The rebel leader Li Zicheng is approaching!" the scout gasped. "He has a large army and many horses. They will be here within an hour!"

Liu Li Jun moved quickly. He called for the battle alarm to be sounded. His men prepared their bows and arrows and steeled themselves for battle. Some of the regiments used Western style muskets, but Liu Li Jun's men were proud of their skills as

Shouts arose from the men as they rallied, determined to defeat the enemy. At that moment, an immense shower of arrows came toward the watchtower. Flaming grenades and arrows rained down as if they came from the sky itself. Liu Li Jun, on the ladder, was in the midst of it. He was hit by several arrows and fell to the ground. Liu Zhang Wei was beside him immediately.

Liu Li Jun is mortally wounded

"Don't move, Brother!" he yelled, panic in his voice. "I will get help for you." "No," his brother gasped in pain. "Stay here with me."

"But I must get help," Liu Zhang Wei protested. "They will have to operate immediately to take out the arrows."

In reply, Liu Li Jun reached up, took hold of an arrow that was lodged in his shoulder and pulled it out, barely suppressing a cry of pain.

"Stop!" cried Liu Zhang Wei. But Liu Li Jun pulled out another arrow, and another. The blood flowed from his wounds.

"Hear me," Liu Li Jun said hoarsely. "With his last breath, our father told me to help you find your way. This is what I am doing."

"But, my brother—"

"You never listen to me, do you?" Liu Li Jun managed a strained smile. "But you must now. Help me remove my uniform."

Liu Zhang Wei wanted to protest, but it was no use. His brother was struggling with his uniform jacket. Liu Zhang Wei helped him take it off.

"Now you," his brother coughed out. "Take off your suit of clothes." Liu Zhang Wei quickly removed his convict's garb while his brother finished disrobing.

"Help me into your clothes, quickly!" insisted Liu Li Jun. "I will die soon. I may as well die a convict." He winced in pain as Liu Zhang Wei guided his arm into a sleeve. "Now put on my uniform. Hurry!"

"Brother, why—" Liu Zhang Wei began.

"You will take my identity," said his brother. "Here is my helmet. Look, the army is retreating. Leave me and go with my regiment. You will not be noticed in the confusion. No one will pay attention to just another soldier running away."

"How can I leave you? You will die here, alone."

"Who knows?" the dying man smiled. "I may have a reward in heaven for this sacrifice. You must live on and work to make our ancestors proud. No dying for you yet. Here, take the belt."

Liu Zhang Wei fastened the belt from his brother's uniform around his waist. It was much too large for him and he wrapped the belt twice around his body. Then he knelt beside where his brother lay on the cold stone floor. He reached under Liu Li Jun's arms and pulled him up into a sitting position as the wounded man coughed up blood. Confusion was all around the brothers as the Ming soldiers retreated. Li Zicheng's rebels climbed over the wall and began to chase down their foes.

Liu Zhang Wei takes on his brother's uniform- and identity

"Now you must go. The battle has been lost and all are running."

"I will not forget you. I will honor your memory and that of our parents, I promise."

"Keep that promise, my brother. No more excuses and lies. You must hold yourself accountable for your actions and good fortune will follow you. Be an honest man. Guard the Dynasty chest and its legacy."

Liu Li Jun held out his helmet for his brother to put on. "Pray that my path to heaven is smooth. Goodbye, *Didi*," he said as he closed his eyes and breathed his last.

Liu Zhang Wei could not bear to leave his brother, but he had to turn away to keep from sobbing. He looked down at the helmet in his hands, and then placed it on his head. He felt changed somehow; stronger and taller. He straightened up and looked at his brother's body, slumped in the dirty clothes of a convict. "I will not waste my life. You will smile on me from heaven. Goodbye, *Gēgē*," he whispered, tears stinging his eyes. He only turned and fled when two soldiers from his brother's regiment pulled him along with them.

The sun rose the next morning on hundreds of dead from each side, their bodies strewn on top of and at the base of the wall. Families retrieved some of the bodies, and high-ranking soldiers were buried properly. The rest were tossed into the unfinished part of the Great Wall, including the body of Lu Li Jun, a hero dressed as a common prisoner.

Liu Zhang Wei escaped into the city. If he'd still been in his convict's clothing, he would have been arrested again or even executed on the street. As it was, he was able to hide in the confusion following the battle. But what next? He considered joining the men who were looting and stealing in the chaos that took over the city. It would be a good chance to fill his empty pockets with some cash. The thought of returning to petty theft was short-lived, however. Liu Zhang Wei had promised his brother that he would live as an honorable man, and he meant to keep that promise. It was his responsibility now to guard the Dynasty chest, so he made his way back home. His father's friend was there, still keeping watch over the house and the Dynasty chest.

Liu Zhang Wei thanked him. "I wish I could pay you for your trouble, but I have no money," he said.

"Honoring the memory of your good father is enough," said the friend as he bowed and took his leave.

The house was sad and empty now. Liu Zhang Wei was sad too, and exhausted from his ordeal. He spent a few days just eating and sleeping, but his dreams were restless. He tossed and turned as he dreamed of saying goodbye to his brother again and again, and then standing in front of his parents and ancestors to answer for all his indiscretions. Liu Zhang Wei was grateful to have his life, but he needed to accomplish something with it. He had to find a way to make his brother's sacrifice worthwhile.

There was talk in the village of changes taking place in Beijing. A new Emperor had been declared, and as long as the people swore allegiance to him, they were welcome in Beijing to seek jobs. Any job, no matter how menial, would be a start, thought Liu Zhang Wei.

But Beijing also had the Emperor's residence—the Forbidden City. He had longed to see the sprawling imperial city ever since he was a boy, watching the lines of elephants marching on their way to serve the Emperor. He had caught glimpses of the high red walls, the moat, and yellow tile roofs when he arrived in Beijing as a prisoner. If only he could get in to the Forbidden City!

Liu Zhang Wei fingered the money tree, still in the pocket of his old robe. This time he would do it right. His blood and sweat, not idle wishing, would create prosperity. He would earn respect. He would bring honor to his parents, his ancestors, and especially his brother. Walking to the family shrine room, he decided to return the money tree to the Dynasty chest. He lifted the lid of the chest, moved a few items and saw the glint of gold. It was the ancient paiza—the golden passport his father had told him about. The Emperor Kublai Khan had given it to Marco Polo, and Polo had given it to their ancestor. It conveyed the blessing of the Khan and guaranteed safe passage to whoever held it. Liu Zhang Wei lifted it from the chest to admire its fine workmanship. It was from a long-ago Dynasty, but it might still impress the new rulers.

Liu Zhang Wei made a decision. He wouldn't settle for an ordinary life working on the outskirts of Beijing. When he put on Liu Li Jun's helmet that terrible day, he had promised to take charge of his life. That moment had changed Liu Zhang Wei, and he would never forget it. He would find his way into the Forbidden City and seek his fortune there. He was prepared to work hard, though. The paiza might grant him entrance, but he wouldn't depend on it for anything else. He would make his own way, with his own sweat and blood.

He took a few days to prepare, and began his journey. Liu Zhang Wei knew he had the trust and love of his father, mother, brother and all his ancestors with him as he walked to Beijing, leading a donkey cart that held his few possessions and the precious Dynasty chest.

— Chapter 6 —

Creating a Life Worth Living

In the few days it took to walk to Beijing, Liu Zhang Wei thought about his ancestors—the way they lived their lives and the things they put in the Dynasty chest to inspire their descendants. He had placed the emblem from his brother's army helmet into the chest, but he had nothing of his own to add. How was it that he, the person in his family least deserving of life, should be the only one left? He was not meant to be the keeper of the Dynasty chest, but it was his responsibility now. He owed it to his brother, his parents and his ancestors to make a life worth living, as they had.

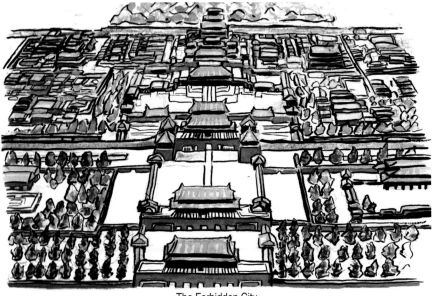

The Forbidden City

Feeling apprehensive as he approached the city, Liu Zhang Wei stopped to rest on a hill overlooking Beijing. While the donkey noisily munched on grass, he removed the paiza from the Dynasty chest and sat under a tree. He didn't know what lay ahead of him. This golden passport might be his ticket to the Forbidden City; the start of a better life. He wanted prosperity and happiness, but now he understood the legend of the money tree. Nothing came for free. His life came at the price of his brother's. And whatever he accomplished, he would remember that.

Liu Zhang Wei patted the donkey as he stood up. He took its reins in one hand and the paiza in the other and walked down the hill, to Beijing and the Forbidden City. The closer he got, the busier it was. Men and women hurried through the streets. Merchants with carts and baskets hawked their wares. Fruits, vegetables, trinkets, clothing and jewelry were all for sale. Liu Zhang Wei slipped the paiza in a bag that he slung over his shoulder. He purchased a bowl of rice from a vendor, leaned against the cart and looked around as he ate.

There were probably a few jobs he could get here in Beijing, he thought. A messenger boy if nothing else; they seemed to be everywhere. Maybe the only job he was fit for was manual labor, like he did on the wall. A job as a goat. These thoughts discouraged the young man until he remembered the paiza, hidden in the cloth bag. No, he had a chance for something better and he had to take it. He wanted to see the wonders of the Forbidden City. If he could get inside, he'd get a job and do his best at it. That was his goal.

Liu Zhang Wei straightened up, took the donkey's reins and continued on his way with new resolve. As he approached the gates of the Forbidden City, he stopped to take the paiza from the bag. Holding it in his hand gave him a little courage. Pretend to be confident, even if you're not, he thought to himself.

He took a deep breath, stood as straight as possible, and walked up to the large, impressive main gate. Armed guards flanked the two heavy red doors, lined with gilded studs, which were set into the red brick walls. They came to attention as Liu Zhang Wei approached, and one spoke. "You there. What is your business?"

Liu Zhang Wei begins his new life

"I wish to enter the Forbidden City." Liu Zhang Wei tried to calm his shaking voice.

"Ha," The man laughed. "Many people wish to enter the Forbidden City but admission is denied most of them. What are you holding there?" he asked. Liu Zhang Wei held the paiza up for him to see. He tried to think of how he would explain what it was, but the guard spoke again.

"Come with me," was all the guard said. He led Liu Zhang Wei through a side gate, and the young man found himself inside the Forbidden City. It was almost as busy inside the gate as it had been outside. Eunuchs, servants, and government workers hurried to and fro. The emperor and his family lived in the inner part of the palace. This outer area bustled with commerce and business. An official with a long Manchu braid hanging down his back walked up to meet the guard.

"This man is in possession of an ancient paiza," said the guard.

The official held out his hand and Liu Zhang Wei handed him the paiza for inspection. "Do you live here in Beijing? How do you happen to have this paiza?" the official asked him.

"I have just arrived in the city," answered Liu Zhang Wei. "The paiza has been in my family for generations. The great Kublai Khan gave it to the explorer Marco Polo, to guarantee him safe passage throughout the empire. When Marco Polo returned to his home, he gave it to my ancestor." Liu Zhang Wei's throat went dry with nervousness, but he swallowed his fear and went on. "I hoped it would allow me to find a job here."

The official handed the paiza back to Liu Zhang Wei. "I am in charge of applications to work in the Forbidden City. The government of the Ming Dynasty is no more. We Manchus are in charge now and most of the work here is done by us. But occasionally we need others. Do you have a trade?"

Liu Zhang Wei gulped again. What would he say? He had no profession, no skills. Why should they let him stay? Before he could think of an answer, shouts came from across the courtyard. A man ran by, yelling "An elephant is loose! It broke away from its keeper! It has gone mad!"

The people in the courtyard ran for cover. Liu Zhang Wei, however, stayed where he was. He remembered how, as a child, he watched the lines of elephants that passed his home on their way to Beijing. He had seen how the keepers handled them, and how they dealt with animals that were injured or sick, and often frightened.

The charging elephant came into view. None of the elephant keepers had been able to catch up to the huge animal. It lumbered into the courtyard, wild with distress and panic. Without hesitation, Liu Zhang Wei stepped in front of the elephant and held up his hand. "Quiet!" he said, as he had seen the elephant handlers do on the road.

To his amazement, the elephant stopped in its tracks. Liu Zhang Wei continued to hold up his hand, and the elephant stood still. After a few moments, two keepers, out of breath from chasing the elephant, rushed forward with chains.

"Be careful," said Liu Zhang Wei to the keepers. "I think this elephant may be injured. "Left," he said to the elephant, gesturing toward his foot. The animal lifted its leg. "You see? There is a wound on the bottom of his foot. Every time he put weight on this foot, the pain increased, and he became more and more agitated as he ran."

"It is lucky you were here," said one of the keepers. "After he broke away, neither of us could get in front of him to command him to stop."

The government official who had examined the paiza returned, leading Liu Zhang Wei's donkey and cart. "You don't have to tell me what your trade is," he said. "I can see you have been trained as an elephant keeper."

"We need another man in the stables," the other keeper said. "When can you start?"

"No, the fault was mine," said Liu Zhang Wei. "Are you visiting the Forbidden City?" he asked.

The young woman sighed. "No. I was brought here a month ago," she explained. "The royal envoys were sent to every village within a day's travel. They chose the most beautiful girls to be concubines of the Prince Regent. The people in my village thought it was a great honor for me." Her voice faltered, and she turned away. "Of course, it is an honor. My parents wanted me to go. I did not cry until after they could no longer see me on the road."

She paused for a moment, sighed again, and continued her story.

"But there are so many young women who were brought here. The Prince Regent hasn't even seen us all yet, and the new Emperor is still a little boy. I may become an old woman just waiting to be called to meet him! He'll be surprised!"

They both laughed. Liu Zhang Wei could see how this young woman was picked as the most beautiful girl in her village. Her face lit up when she smiled, and she moved and gestured with a lovely, easy grace.

"We are kept busy as maids, and most of the other servants and concubines are kind to us," she added. "I just wanted to be alone for a while today. I figured out how to slip away from my quarters without anyone noticing. I may be scolded when I go back, but it will be worth it."

The young woman looked up into the trees and took a deep breath of the scented air, made fragrant by the large incense burners scattered about. She then turned back to Liu Zhang Wei. "What do you do here in the Forbidden City?" she asked him. "Are you a servant?"

"I am an elephant keeper. I've only been here a few months myself," he answered.

"Do you come to the Imperial Gardens often?" she wondered. "The gardens are a good distance away from the elephant stables."

"I come to the gardens whenever I get a chance. I enjoy working with the elephants. They're such majestic creatures. But the flowers and the incense smell much better than the stables."

She laughed. "Then it is worth the walk."

"It was worth twice the walk today, having met you. My name is Liu Zhang Wei." "I am Xun Ai," she said with a shy smile.

As the weeks passed, Liu Zhang Wei and Xun Ai met often in the gardens. Xun Ai was a sweet and understanding young woman. They often talked about their families and life back in their villages. As they grew closer, Liu Zhang Wei even told Xun Ai about his own past and the mistakes he had made. He told her about the Dynasty chest and brought small treasures from it to share with her. It became a happy ritual. They would meet in the gardens and find a private place to talk. Liu Zhang Wei would show Xun Ai a trinket he had brought from the Dynasty chest, and tell her the story behind it. Then they would talk and dream about their own hopes for the future. They were falling in love.

All this time, Xun Ai had not been called to appear before the court. "It's been almost four months. Maybe they have forgotten about me," she wondered one day as she and Liu Zhang Wei sat by a pond in their favorite part of the garden. "The Prince Regent must have all the concubines he desires."

Liu Zhang Wei put his arm around her. "You should be able to have a life of your own," he said. "You should not have to live at the whim of the Prince Regent. Every person deserves happiness. Every person deserves a chance to build a life and a legacy of their own." Liu Zhang Wei had learned this from his wise father, his brother, and the legacy his ancestors had left in the Dynasty chest. He continued, holding Xun Ai's hands. "If you are happy with me, and I with you, then we should be together. I love you."

"And I love you," she said. "But I am afraid. We are not allowed to be together."

"The chest is full of things from my ancestors. There's no room for anything of mine."

"But don't you have a life worth living? What about your legacy? What about your hopes and dreams?"

Liu Zhang Wei smiled at Xun Ai. "You are right, my wife. You and I must live in secret until you are old enough to be released from the Forbidden City. But that doesn't mean our lives aren't worth living." He looked up into the setting sun and said, "I deserve a legacy too. I will build my own Dynasty chest." He put his arms around Xun Ai and held her close.

Building the War chest

Liu Zhang Wei built his own chest, a sturdy box of strong black wood. He thought of his brother every day and the sacrifice that Liu Li Jun had made in giving up his life. This chest must honor the memory of my brother, he thought. I wouldn't be alive to put anything in it if it wasn't for him. Liu Zhang Wei inlaid the front, back and sides of the chest with black wood pieces in a studded pattern that looked like the front of his brother's army uniform. He called it the War chest. It would always remind him to live up to the hope his brother had placed in him.

Having the War chest made Liu Zhang Wei even more impatient to live openly with Xun Ai. It would be a few years yet before she was released, and it was hard to wait. Soon, however, there was another complication. Xun Ai became pregnant. It was wonderful and terrifying at the same time. A child had been conceived by their love, and it gave them joy. But they had to find a way to conceal the pregnancy and keep the baby safe. Xun Ai thought of a plan.

"Not far from here are the apartments where the wet nurses live," she explained to Liu Zhang Wei. "I will say that I am ill, and keep myself hidden in my room as much as I can. When the baby is born, Meimei will take it to one of the wet nurses she knows. The wet nurse will care for the child until we can finally leave the city."

"I am glad we have trusted Meimei," said Liu Zhang Wei. "She is a good friend to both of us."

"Yes," agreed Xun Ai. "So far we have escaped notice, with her help. I pray that our luck lasts a while longer."

Xun Ai stayed indoors for the next several months, feigning illness, and Meimei helped her conceal her growing pregnancy. It was impossible to hide completely, though, and a few girls in the concubines' quarters suspected that Xun Ai was pregnant. One girl thought she had seen a man leaving Xun Ai's room.

Xun Ai was unaware of the suspicion. She was looking forward to the day she would hold her baby in her arms and how proud Liu Zhang Wei would be of their child. Her pregnancy went smoothly, but she went into labor a few weeks before she thought she would. There was no way to contact Liu Zhang Wei, who was on the other side of the city.

— Chapter 7 —

Father and Daughter Build a Legacy

The news spread throughout the Forbidden City. By noon, Liu Zhang Wei heard that a concubine had been executed that morning. His mind went numb. As soon as he could, he left the elephant stables. He made his way to the rendezvous point; the place Meimei always met him when it was safe to visit Xun Ai. He waited there on a stone bench. It was a beautiful spot on the edge of the Imperial Gardens, with blossoming plum trees and incense burners. But Liu Zhang Wei shut everything out of his mind. He tried not to see, hear, or feel anything; not till he had to. He waited an hour and a half, staring into the plum blossoms, before Meimei appeared.

She did not need to speak. One look at her face told him everything. Xun Ai was gone. She was the concubine who had been executed.

"No," he whispered as he stood. It hurt to speak; it hurt to breathe. His life was over. "I can't let her go. I can't let her be alone. I must—I must find a way to kill myself now, so I can be with her." His desperate breath came in short gasps. The pain was unbearable.

Meimei grabbed him by the shoulders and shook, hard. "No! You will not kill yourself. Look at me. You have a daughter! The baby was born. You have a daughter who needs you!"

The cloud began to lift from Liu Zhang Wei's eyes. "What?"

"The child was born early this morning, and she is safe! I told the eunuchs she was dead, and after they left with Xun Ai, I took the baby to the wet nurse."

"The baby is a girl?" Liu Zhang Wei saw a ray of hope break through his storm of grief.

"Yes," Meimei smiled, in spite of everything. "You have a beautiful baby girl. She will bring honor to her mother."

Liu Zhang Wei nodded. The wave of pain subsided a little, and he lowered himself on the bench. Meimei joined him and they sat together in silence for several minutes, listening to the rushing of the water in the fountains. Finally Liu Zhang Wei stood up.

"Thank you, Meimei. You helped us so much already, and now my child lives because of you."

"I loved Xun Ai too," said Meimei, her eyes brimming with tears. "But we will have to grieve for her alone and silently. Come back to this spot in two weeks, at the usual time. I will try to bring the baby to you."

Liu Zhang Wei spent the next two weeks in a haze, feeling everything and feeling nothing at the same time. Regret, sorrow and guilt mixed with his memories of happiness and joy. He went about his duties as usual, which helped pass the time. As he made his way toward the rendezvous point on the appointed day, he thought about his child. A baby girl. Would she look like Xun Ai? Would that make him happy? Or would it break his heart even more?

Meimei was already sitting on the bench under the plum tree when he arrived. She stood and handed him the squirming bundle that was his daughter. "Here she is," she said. "Isn't she beautiful? The wet nurse says she eats well, sleeps soundly and cries loudly. That's good."

Liu Zhang Wei held the baby and looked into her face. Even at only two weeks old, she reminded him of Xun Ai. She was bright-eyed, alert and strong. Almost overcome with a mixture of joy and sadness, he kissed the baby's chubby cheeks and turned to Meimei.

"What becomes of us now?" Liu Zhang Wei asked as he sat on the bench and positioned the baby on his lap.

"The wet nurse will continue to care for her as long as you want her to," said Meimei. "She says the child is an easy baby."

Meimei watched as Liu Zhang Wei gazed at his daughter with tender love. Thinking of Xun Ai, her eyes filled with tears. "I think she must be so sweet and happy because she was born out of a love that overcame great obstacles," she said at last. "But you must think of a name for her. We have been calling her Kuàilè Bǎobǎo. She needs a better name than just Happy Baby."

"Liu Li Juan will be her name," decided Liu Zhang Wei. "It means beautiful. And I will see to it that she always will be happy." He looked at Meimei and pleaded, "Please let me hold her for a few more minutes before you have to take her back."

Meimei reassured him, "She will know that you are her father. You will see her as often as we can arrange it, and you will tell her about Xun Ai and the love you had."

Liu Zhang Wei gave his daughter another kiss and handed her to Meimei. The only thing he looked forward to now was the next time he would see her. It was now 1648. He had been in the Forbidden City for almost four years. His love, Xun Ai, had been cruelly taken away from him, and his little daughter was all he had left in the world. This child would be his world now, and he would spend every spare minute with her.

Liu Li Juan continued to live with the wet nurse, and as the months passed, anyone who saw the child assumed that she was the wet nurse's daughter. Liu Zhang Wei was confident that she was safe. As she grew, Liu Li Juan looked forward to the time she spent with her father as much as he did. He showed her the elephant stables, and she clapped and giggled with glee when the elephants had their baths. They rode elephants together and often spent afternoons in the Imperial Gardens. Just as he had done with Xun Ai, Liu Zhang Wei showed his daughter precious items from the Dynasty chest and from his own War chest as well. He had placed the emblem from his brother's helmet in his chest, jewelry and trinkets that had belonged to Xun Ai, and a pair of Liu Li Juan's baby slippers. He also had some pen and ink pictures that Xun Ai had drawn. Liu Li Juan loved looking at those. She liked to draw her own, trying to imitate her mother.

Liu Li Juan was a happy and good natured child, and she was a favorite playmate of the children in "Wet Nurse Lane." The wet nurses cared for the babies of concubines and consorts until the children were weaned. On a summer day in 1653, when Liu Li Juan was five years old, one of the higher-ranking consort's sons was ready to be returned to his mother after having been weaned. To everyone's dismay, the child screamed and cried when he was told it was time to go away with his mother. Liu Li Juan had been his playmate and companion for the last year and he did not want to leave her. The only way he would go with his mother was if Liu Li Juan went with him. The wet nurse consented as long as the little girl came back that evening after the boy had gone to bed. She knew that Liu Zhang Wei would be expecting to visit his daughter. From then on, Liu Li Juan spent her days in the concubines' quarters playing with the children there, and seeing her father at the wet nurse's apartment in the evenings.

After a few months of this arrangement, the wet nurse approached Liu Zhang Wei with an idea. He had arrived early one afternoon, and Liu Li Juan had not yet returned from the concubines' quarters. The wet nurse explained to Liu Zhang Wei, "The children your daughter plays with will soon be going to school. Even the girls will be taught to read and write if their mothers wish it. You should take advantage of this. I'll tell the schoolteacher that Liu Li Juan should learn to read and write along with the other girls. I'll explain that they won't be able to concentrate if she is not with them, since Liu Li Juan is their favorite playmate."

"It is a wonderful opportunity," agreed Liu Zhang Wei. "If my daughter learns to read and write, a whole new world will be opened to her."

Liu Li Juan thrived in school, quickly learning her lessons and pleasing the teachers. By the time she was eight years old, she was graceful and charming, looking more and more like her mother every day. "Méihuā," Liu Zhang Wei said to his daughter one afternoon while they were in the gardens. "Come and sit down beside me."

Liu Li Juan skipped over to her father to show him a drawing she had made of a flower. "Look, Father," the little girl said. "It's a plum blossom. And I can write the word underneath it. See?"

Liu Zhang Wei took the drawing in his hand. "I'm very proud of your writing and drawing," he said. "You are my own little plum blossom. That's why I call you Méihuā."

The memories flooded back to Liu Zhang Wei, as they often did, of times when he and Xun Ai would wander through the gardens, sit on a stone bench to kiss and then lean back and stare up into the sun shining through the pink plum blossoms, her head resting on his shoulder.

It was a sad and sweet memory, but Liu Zhang Wei was happy. He had his little blossom here with him, and she made him more determined than ever to have a life worth living. He looked around at the flowering plum trees, and thought of how the blossoms symbolized resilience and perseverance in the face of adversity during the harsh winter. He had faced adversity, surely. But with his daughter he would persevere.

"Thank you, Father," said Liu Li Juan as she admired the workmanship. "It is a beautiful chest. May I open it?"

"Yes," said Lu Zhang Wei. His daughter opened the lid. "I have already put a few things in it for you. Here is a little fan you played with when you were tiny."

"I remember, Father," she said, smiling.

"Here is an elephant figurine. Its trunk is up, for good luck. And here is a jade hairpin. It belonged to your mother. In fact, she was wearing it the day we met." He smiled at the sweet memory. "Now do you have anything to put in your chest, daughter? Or are you too young to have any memories yet?" he said, teasing her.

"Oh, I have a few," she said. "Remember when I was nine years old, and the little prince said he was in love with me? He gave me a tiny dog carved out of ivory. And he made me promise to feed it every day so it would grow to be a giant ivory dog." She laughed. "I will keep that in my Blossom chest. I also have some school examination papers that I scored well on. They will be safe there."

"You are an accomplished scholar, my daughter," said Liu Zhang Wei. "I am proud of you. You have learned everything that is allowed for girls to study."

"And some things that only boys are allowed to study, Father," said Liu Li Juan. "I went with the little prince to his classes for quite a few years. No one seemed to mind that I was learning the same things the boys were."

"You do have a unique education then, Daughter," said the proud father.

"Yes, Father. And it has given me a unique opportunity. More and more of the girls in the Imperial family are learning to read and write. The teacher who is in charge of the children's education has asked me to be an official instructor. I will teach all the young children, girls and boys, their beginning reading lessons and then teach the older girls reading and writing both. It is a position of great honor, Father. Shall I accept?"

"If it will make you happy to do this, yes. Accept the position. You are the designer of your own life, my daughter. You are free to live the way you think is best." Liu Zhang Wei looked at his daughter's beautiful eyes, so like her mother's. He wanted her to have the happy life that Xun Ai could not have. "Liu Li Juan, whenever you have a decision to make, think about what you want your legacy to be. Think of what you want your descendants to find in your Blossom chest after you have passed. That will help you decide what to do today, and tomorrow."

"Thank you, Father. I will accept the position. Teaching the Imperial family's children will make me very proud and happy."

"Will you teach them about my elephants? That would make me very happy," said Liu Zhang Wei.

"Oh, they love elephants. I may be able to get permission to bring some of them out to the stables to watch the elephants get their baths. Now, Father, I must return to my quarters with the Blossom chest. Is it very heavy?"

"I will carry it home for you. Soon you will be living in the Imperial family residence. Make sure you find a place of honor for your Blossom chest." Liu Zhang Wei grunted as he picked up the chest. "Will you still have time to visit with your old elephant daddy some evenings?"

"Yes, Daddy. I will make sure that we have time together. We will keep the fig tree watered."

Father and daughter did keep the fig tree watered. Over the years, they worked at their jobs in the Forbidden City, spent time together, and made memories for the War chest and the Blossom chest.

Eventually Liu Li Juan left the Forbidden City. On one of her visits to her father at the elephant stables when she was twenty-two years old, she met an elephant broker from Shanghai. They eventually fell in love, and he asked her to marry him. Her life in the Forbidden City was all she had known, and she was unsure of what to do. She had a fine position as teacher to the Imperial family's children. She didn't want to upset or anger anyone by leaving. But she knew she loved the young man and wanted to be with him, and remembering that she was the designer of her own life, said yes. Her confidence and resolve shone through when she asked permission to leave the Forbidden City, and it was granted. She took her Blossom chest and its memories, kissed her father goodbye, and started her new life.

It was a time of change for Liu Zhang Wei as well. His destiny had been in the Forbidden City. It was where he had found his love and raised his daughter. Liu Li Juan's destiny would be outside the Forbidden City. She would make her own way and create a life worth living. It was hard to say goodbye, but Liu Zhang Wei was proud of his daughter and happy for her.

When her children were born, Liu Li Juan was able to come back to the Forbidden City to visit her father and let him see his grandchildren. The first baby was born in 1674, when Liu Zhang Wei was 56 years old. He was a very attentive grandfather to Sun Zhang Lei.

"You were born in the year of the Tiger, little one," Liu Zhang Wei said as he bounced the baby on his knee. "Grr, grr, grr!" The baby laughed and gurgled. "That's right, growl like a tiger. I will get you a tiger figurine and you can put it into your very own chest someday."

"This child will be the chest keeper for our family, Father," Liu Li Juan said. "I will teach him to take care of your father's Dynasty chest, your War chest, and my Blossom chest, as well as his own."

"Thank you, Daughter," said Liu Zhang Wei. I know you will teach him well." As father and daughter embraced, the next Dynasty chest keeper growled and giggled as he played at being a baby tiger.

After a few hours of visiting and drinking tea, Liu Zhang Wei waved goodbye to Liu Li Juan and the baby. He was content. His daughter had her own family and was happy. She was filling her Blossom chest with memories.

At age 58, Liu Zhang Wei became the head elephant keeper. Ten years later he retired, an honored and respected elder. By his 80th year, he spent most of his days resting and reminiscing. He remembered the events in his life by looking at the treasures in the Dynasty chest and the War chest. When he died in 1702, his daughter was notified. She then became the family chest keeper, and would eventually hand down the responsibility to her oldest child, Sun Zhang Lei.

Marco Polo began the tradition when he gave the original Dynasty chest to Gurmi, his Sherpa guide. Gurmi's descendants handed down the chest, each adding to its contents. Liu Zhang Wei expanded on the legacy by building the War chest for himself and the Blossom chest for Liu Li Juan. She would hand down the family's chests to her son, and he would become that generation's chest keeper, adding his own and being responsible for all the chests that came before. Each generation would continue the tradition and be inspired by the legacy.

Part Two

Stories of Ten Chests

the gardens with them and telling the story of the day her father gave her the Blossom chest.

One afternoon while visiting the Forbidden City, she sat with Sun Zhang Lei in a shady part of the Imperial Garden. "You are my oldest child, and will soon be a man. You will be responsible for the care of our family's legacy: the ancient Dynasty chest, my father's War chest, and my Blossom chest. My son, you will also create a chest, one that you will fill with *your* legacy."

Her son interrupted her. "Mother, I am honored to be the chest keeper. I'll take the responsibility seriously. You need not worry about our family's legacy."

His mother frowned. "I am not worried about the chests. I know you will honor the legacy and keep them safe. What I am worried about is your own legacy. You push ahead without regard, like an untrained elephant. Do you not notice that even your parents must fight to get a word in during a conversation with you? My son, you must learn to listen as well as talk."

"But, Mother," Sun Zhang Lei interrupted again. "Most people have nothing intelligent to say."

"Even your own mother?" she softly chided. "You would be surprised at how much others have to offer when you set your ego aside."

"I am sorry," Sun Zhang Lei lowered his head for a moment. "I will try to do better in the future. I want to be the best man I can be."

Liu Li Juan placed her small hand on top of her son's large one. "I know, my son. But you take yourself too seriously. I saw when your younger brother teased you last night. You were so angry with him you almost knocked him over in your hurry to leave the room. Try to remember what I have said. There is much to learn from and appreciate in your fellow man. You need not always be the tallest, the strongest and the smartest. The more people you can learn from, the richer your legacy will be."

Sun Zhang Lei tried to remember what his mother told him, but he struggled with the idea. He really did always want to be the tallest, the strongest and the smartest. And when anyone said or did anything to make it look like he wasn't, he became frustrated and angry.

He had a hard time getting along with people, but Sun Zhang Lei loved the elephants his father worked with. His strength and confidence made him fearless around the huge beasts. He was a young man, just barely twenty years old, but he assisted his father with the business and often delivered elephants to the Forbidden City.

Sometimes when they traveled to the Forbidden City, Sun Zhang Lei spent time in the elephant stables with the trainers. He bragged about how his grandfather had been the head elephant trainer.

"My grandfather had a natural way with the elephants. If I wanted to, I could walk in and be a better trainer than any man here," he often boasted. Sun Zhang Lei always had to act like the tallest, the strongest, and the smartest, even though it wasn't always true.

The men always shook their heads when they saw him swaggering toward the stables. "Here he comes," they would groan. "The braggart. His big head will cause him big problems," they predicted.

One day Sun Zhang Lei and his father were in charge of delivering a half-dozen elephants to the Forbidden City. They approached the crowded square just outside the main gate, where vendors and townspeople gathered. The square was busy and crowded with people. The trainers' helpers went ahead to announce that a line of elephants was preparing to cross the square to the main gate of the Forbidden City.

After getting the signal from the trainers' helpers, Sun Zhang Lei began to lead the elephants across the courtyard. He stood straight and tall as he commanded the animals, enjoying the admiring glances from the onlookers. All at once, however, a young child shot out from a group of children that had been safely watching the procession from a terrace. The little boy wanted to see an elephant up close and his mother could not stop him before he ran down the steps and straight toward the lumbering beasts. If the elephants were startled, they could break rank and cause havoc. Or if the little boy slipped, he could fall underneath an elephant's foot.

Sun Zhang Lei heard the onlookers yell to the little boy. Moving quickly, he scooped the child up in his arms and spun away from the path of the elephants. A cheer rose from the crowd as Sun Zhang Lei handed the boy over to his mother. All was well and he was a hero! He waved to the crowd and felt a surge of pride. He then stepped back and turned to receive more applause, but suddenly lost his balance. The crowd yelled again, but for a different reason. Sun Zhang Lei had backed into a koi pond! His arms flailed as he tried to regain his balance, but it was no use. He crashed into the water, making a huge splash. The elephants marched past as he sat in the pond, with everyone in the square watching, pointing and howling with laughter.

Sun Zhang Lei struggled to stand on the slippery bottom of the pool and yelled, "How dare you laugh at me! After I saved that child! Don't you know who I am?"

His temper tantrum only made him look funnier and the crowd laughed louder. Even the little boy that he had saved was laughing at him. Sun Zhang Lei climbed out of the pond and stomped after the elephants, dripping water. He was humiliated and angry. As soon as the elephants were safely inside the stables, Sun Zhang Lei left without talking to anyone, even his father. He wanted to get out of the Forbidden City and the market square as soon as possible. How would he ever face those people again? he thought to himself as the sun dried his clothes during the long walk back.

At home, nothing was said about the incident, but Sun Zhang Lei noticed his father whispering to his mother. Later that night, his mother invited him to sit down for tea. Sun Zhang Lei was anxious to tell his mother about the horrible event he had endured, and how awful it was that people had laughed at him. Surely his mother would agree that those people should have shown him more respect.

As he entered the room, he noticed his mother smiling at him. It was an odd smile, though. There was a twinkle in her eyes that he remembered from when he was a boy. He sat down. She handed him a tea cup. He lifted it to his lips but stopped just in time. Looking inside, he saw a tiny fish swimming in water in the tea cup. Sun Zhang Lei looked up at his mother and she burst out laughing. Even his mother! His face got red with anger and embarrassment. He was about to protest this unfair treatment when something finally gave way in his spirit. He pictured how silly he must have looked in the koi pond, and began to laugh along with his mother.

"Son, this laughter is good," his mother said. "If you cannot laugh at yourself, you will never be truly happy."

"Thank you, Mother," said Sun Zhang Lei. "I am finally beginning to understand."

"I am glad to hear it," said his mother with a smile. "To be able to laugh at yourself, you need to set aside your ego. Leave it at the door in your encounters with others. You have confidence to spare, my son. People will still respect you when you make a mistake. They may even respect you more for being able to laugh at yourself." She smiled again and poured him another cup of tea. "Don't worry! This one does not have a fish in it!" she said.

Sun Zhang Lei appreciated the advice from his mother, and tried to check his swaggering ego at the door as she had wisely advised. It took some practice, but he was eventually able to listen to and learn from others. He gained true respect from his friends and colleagues. In fact, a lovely and intelligent young woman took a fancy to him. She especially liked his easy-going nature and the fact that he could laugh at himself!

When he moved into his own home, Sun Zhang Lei had a chest built for himself. It was a simple but elegant square chest with brass metal strips for trim and a brass circle on the front, the design of which looked like decorations in the Forbidden City. He called his chest the "Forbidden City chest", in honor of his mother and his grandparents. He wanted it to remind him of their focus on relationships and the importance of others, not self. Sun Zhang Lei received the original Dynasty chest and the other family chests at the age of fifty-three, when his mother died in 1727. He took his mother's tea cup that had held the little fish and kept it in his chest as a reminder to keep his ego in check.

The Contentment Chest

Sun Wang Min, the first child of Sun Zhang Lei, was the next chest keeper, born in 1697. Sun Wang Min was always a dreamy girl. She lived a pleasant life with her father and mother in a modest home outside Beijing, where her father raised and brokered elephants for trade. She had many friends, and as she grew older several young men expressed interest in her as a possible wife. Many girls would have considered Sun Wang Min to be a lucky and fortunate girl. But her dreams and fantasies took up most of her time and energy. She was never satisfied with things the way they were. She longed for a glamorous life in Beijing and thought about nothing else but living there. Marrying a nice young man and staying in a small town would be settling for much less than what she wanted.

Since Sun Wang Min was so unhappy and dissatisfied, she was unable to see any of the beauty and goodness around her, including the value of a young man who persisted in courting her. She liked him and finally said yes to his proposal, but never truly enjoyed being with him. Her thoughts were consumed with how different her life would be if she was in the city. If only I had more money, she would often think to herself. I could live in Beijing and my life would be wonderful!

Sun Wang Min had built up her fantasy world to such an extent that she lived in it more than she lived in the real world. She was often distracted and impatient with people who pulled her out of her imagination. Even her fiancé felt neglected. The only time she paid attention to him was when she tried to change something about him, such as his hairstyle or his clothing.

Another couple invited Sun Wang Min and her fiancé to a gambling parlor one evening. They had an enjoyable time and Sun Wang Min won a little money. It was exciting for her to be in a gambling parlor. Over the next several days, she couldn't stop thinking about what a wonderful future she would have if she were lucky enough to win a big jackpot! Sun Wang Min began to frequent the gambling house. When her fiancé or friends didn't want to go, she went alone. She began to gamble more and more often, and she lied to her family and friends about how much money she was losing. The young woman was desperate to hit a big jackpot, and was certain life would be perfect when it came.

Early one evening her fiancé came to see her, but Sun Wang Min was not at home. Her parents thought she was out with a girlfriend, but the friend said they had made no plans. Her worried fiancé had a hunch and went to the gambling parlor. There he found Sun Wang Min. When he asked her to stop gambling and come home, Sun Wang Min lashed out at him. "My time is my own and so is my money!" she said harshly. "I can choose what I want to do with it. I'm so unhappy, and no one understands me or what I want!"

"Yes, I think I do understand," said her fiancé. "You want things that are impossible to get. You want perfection; a fantasy world, a world filled with mythical charms and probably mythical people too. I don't fit in that world, but you would rather live there than be with me. Stay here at the gambling parlor as long as you like. I will come to your home tomorrow to discuss breaking our engagement."

Sun Wang Min was furious as she watched her fiancé leave. He was being unfair. She just wanted a better life. What was wrong with that? She thought about following him, but turned back to the gambling table and shut out all troubling thoughts— until she was out of money. With an empty purse, she got up from the table knowing something was terribly wrong, but not at all sure what to do about it. Not long after she had begun her walk home, Sun Wang Min noticed a lone token at the bottom of her purse. She wasn't broke after all! She turned to head back to the gambling house, but a thought struck her. What was she doing? Her fiancé was ready to break their engagement, and all she could think about was trying to strike it rich at the gambling parlor. What would really happen if she went back? She would lay down the one measly token, lose it, and nothing would change. She finally realized that she was deceiving herself.

Sun Wang Min stopped at a bench and wearily sat down. If she couldn't create the life she wanted by gambling, then what could she do? She leaned back and closed her eyes in despair. Then she heard a faint, gentle laugh which made her sit up and look for its source.

Across the path was another bench. An elderly husband and wife were slowly approaching it, hand in hand. The man was walking with a cane and the woman carried a tattered parasol. They were dressed in worn, simple clothes. At first glance, Sun Wang Min felt sorry for them. Here were two old people who lived in poverty and had nothing to show for their lives. She continued to watch as they sat and rested on the bench across from her. The husband held his wife's parasol as she helped him lower himself onto the bench. They didn't speak much as they cuddled together, but now and then one of them pointed to an orange cloud in the darkening sky or a pretty pigeon that landed near their bench.

Sun Wang Min sat and watched the old couple for much longer than she had intended to. Her pity for them changed to admiration and then, surprisingly, envy. They were enjoying each other's company immensely, and enjoying the world around them. They obviously didn't have much money, but they valued each other and this moment together.

What did she have? Nothing but her dream of the future and the gambling token in her hand.

Sun Wang Min took her gaze away from the old couple and looked around her. She was young and healthy but she hadn't appreciated it. The sky, the path, the trees, and the weather were all beautiful but she hadn't noticed it. Her fiancé loved her but she hadn't valued it. She realized that she was wasting the present by only living in the future. Sad and ashamed of herself, Sun Wang Min took one last look at the happy elders and made her way home.

Her mother was glad to see her, but didn't know what to say, especially after noticing the sad look on her daughter's face. After she greeted her mother, Sun Wang Min looked for her father. He was sitting outside in the garden under a catalpa tree.

"Father, please help me," she said.

"Sit down, Daughter. What is wrong?"

Sun Wang Min joined her father on the wooden bench. "I am confused, Father. I feel like I am losing everything. My fiancé, Wang Jie, is reconsidering our engagement. I am unsettled and discontent. I don't know how to be happy."

"What do you want in your life?" her father asked.

"I want to marry Wang Jie and live in Beijing. I would like to raise my children there, so I can show them the beauty and culture of the city."

"That is a fine goal. What is preventing it?"

"Wang Jie does not yet have the connections to start a business in Beijing. It will take hard work and finances. I can't bear the thought of living in this small town for years. I want so badly to leave now. But we don't have the money."

"So, that is why you have been gambling," her father said gently, putting his hand on her arm.

"If only I could win. Then we would have enough money to move to the city and my life would finally be happy. But Wang Jie does not understand. He is ready to break our engagement if I do not stop gambling."

"I do not think it is only the gambling that he is worried about," said her father. "My daughter, your attention is only on the future. To have a happy and balanced life, you must be able to live in the present. Are there no things in your life right now that you can be happy about?"

Sun Wang Min thought for a moment before she spoke. "Of course there are, Father. I am happy to be with my fiancé. I am happy to have you and Mother. I enjoy my friends and I have good health. Oh, Father, there are plenty of things in my life that should give me happiness, but I still feel such discontent. What is wrong with me?"

"Nothing is wrong with you, Daughter," her father said, patting her hand again. "But you need to change your habits. Your practice has been to focus your attention on the future and think that you can only be happy when that future comes. This must change. You must learn to appreciate the good things you have now. These lessons are hard to learn, I know. I had to learn difficult truths as a young man, but my mother did not give up on me, and I learned my lesson: to listen to and value other people without my ego getting in the way. Your lesson is different. You must learn to listen to and value the present moment. It does not mean that you must abandon your plans for the future. I want you to learn to be happy and content in the present while still planning for the future."

Sun Zhang Lei smiled at his first child. "I am building a family chest to give to you when you marry. It will help you find the balance between the past, the present and the future. You may place things in it that hold childhood memories, to honor the past. It can also store items that inspire you to build the future you want to have. The fan I gave you when we traveled to the city to see the opera—keep that in your chest to remind you of your desire to live in Beijing someday."

"But, Father," Sun Wang Min asked, "What can I put in my chest that will honor the present and help me to be content in the moment?"

"You will find things once you start to appreciate the present. Look around you right now: the cool breeze, the setting sun, the leaves of the catalpa tree, a heartfelt conversation between father and daughter. There are so many things to appreciate in the present moment. You will learn."

Sun Wang Min embraced her father impulsively. "Father, your wisdom has given me hope. Gambling has made me unhappy and dissatisfied, but it was my lack of joy and appreciation of what I have now that caused me to turn to gambling in the first place. I will practice appreciating the present, especially when I feel the urge to go to the gambling parlor. But will I be able to make my fiancé understand, Father? I want him to trust me again and not break our engagement. I wish to be happy with him in the present while we work toward our future life together."

"I will talk to him. I know you are sincere in your change of heart," her father assured her. He stood, smiling down on his daughter. "I am glad you have decided to stop gambling, for your sake and for the sake of the family legacy. You will be the family chest keeper, and now I am confident that you will bear the responsibility well."

"Thank you, Father," said Sun Wang Min. "You will be proud of me, I promise."

"After our evening meal tonight, let us begin to build your own chest," said Sun Zhang Lei. "The task of building it will also help you to stay focused on the present. First we must choose the design and the wood."

"I want my chest to look fresh and new," said Sun Wang Min as they walked into the house together. "It must be beautiful now and still be considered beautiful fifty years from now. Not locked into the past or only focused on the future, but to be able to move with the present."

They created a beautiful red chest with angled corners and gold trim. When it was completed, Sun Wang Min knew she would be proud of it her entire life. She took the gambling token that had been in her purse the night she saw the elderly couple on the bench and put it in her chest, which she named "Contentment". It would always remind her to be content in the present while working toward the future.

The Centering Chest

In the year 1728, the year of the monkey, a lively baby was born. He was Sun Wang Min's first child, Wang Zhang Yong. His parents said it was certainly right that he was born in the year of the monkey, because he was a little monkey himself! He climbed on everything, did flips and somersaults and loved playing silly games. He led the neighborhood children in games of follow the leader until they couldn't keep up with his antics anymore.

The young boy's skill at acrobatics caught the attention of an opera master who asked his parents to allow Wang Zhang Yong to become his apprentice. His mother was very excited by this prospect. She and her husband had achieved their dream of living in Beijing after years of hard work, planning and saving. She loved the opera and was proud to think that her son might become a professional performer.

Wang Zhang Yong began his apprenticeship at ten years old. It would take several years of training to learn and polish the acrobatics, martial arts, acting and singing skills he would need.

The students lived at the school but were allowed home for visits on holidays. Wang Zhang Yong came home to visit his parents for the Mid-autumn Festival when he was fifteen. After sitting down to tea and moon cakes, his mother excitedly asked him how his training was progressing.

"I am doing well, Mother," he said. "But there is so much to learn. I think I am best at the acrobatics."

"Of course," smiled his mother. "You were always such a little monkey growing up. Do you remember when you climbed the tallest tree in the neighborhood and all the children wanted to follow you up there? One of the mothers scolded your friend Wei Wei and said, 'If Wang Zhang Yong jumped off the roof, would you do it too?'"

They both laughed, remembering the story.

"Do you remember what he answered?" asked Wang Zhang Yong.

"Certainly," said his mother. "He said, 'Of course I would! I want to do everything that Wang Zhang Yong does!'" Sun Wang Min smiled, remembering. "Everyone in the neighborhood knew you as the monkey boy. The opera master came to see us not long after that."

"I wish all the training was as easy as climbing trees and doing somersaults," said Wang Zhang Yong. "It frustrates me to have to do everything so precisely. I have been learning a routine in which I use a large staff. If I make one mistake, my instructor tells me to go back to the beginning and start again. I've never been able to get through the whole routine. I wonder if I ever will."

"My son, born in the year of the monkey." Sun Wang Min shook her head. "It certainly describes you. Not only do you move like a monkey, but your mind works like one. You must learn to concentrate on one thing at a time."

"It is true, Mother," her son answered. "My thoughts jump around from branch to branch like a monkey on a tree. The staff routine is very long and complicated. It is difficult for me to stay focused."

"Do you still desire to perform in the opera?" asked his mother. "Or do you want to end your apprenticeship?"

"I desire it very much, but I fear I am becoming a disappointment to my teacher."

"Go and speak with your teacher. Ask him for advice on mastering this routine and improving your focus. It is not a sign of weakness to ask for help. Your instructor is a good man and he wants you to be successful."

"Thank you, Mother," said Wang Zhang Yong as he stood up. "I will meet with my instructor as soon as possible."

"His mother stood up as well. "Before you go, come into the shrine room. Your father has finished building your own chest. We will keep it here at home until you are done with your apprenticeship, but I thought you would like to see it now."

Wang Zhang Yong followed his mother into the family shrine room where the chests were kept. Being the oldest child, he would be responsible for the family legacy that was stored in this room. Now, with his chest, there were six: the original Dynasty chest handed down from Marco Polo; the War chest belonging to his great-great-grandfather; the Blossom chest of his great-grandmother; the Forbidden City chest of his grandfather; his mother's Contentment chest; and soon, his own.

On his last visit, Wang Zhang Yong and his father had discussed what he wanted his chest to look like. The finished product was very handsome and was just what he had in mind. The chest was a rich polished dark wood. It had a distinctive and dramatic vine and leaf design executed in gold which covered the exterior.

Wang Zhang Yong ran his hand over the lid of the chest, feeling the coolness of the highly polished wood. "Father did a wonderful job. This chest will inspire me to do my best in my training," he said.

"And it will hold many memories of your career in the opera," said his mother. "Now let us go to your father so you can thank him for the chest. It is time for him to wake up from his nap."

Back at the training school, Wang Zhang Yong sat down to talk with his instructor. He explained his difficulty with the staff routine and told his teacher about how he always had trouble concentrating on one thing at a time.

"I will tell you a story," said his teacher. "Listen well."

There was once a warlord who found himself facing an army ten times larger than his own. His men were frightened. Hopeless, they came to him and asked how they could possibly survive such an uneven battle.

"Here is how it will be done," said the wise warlord. "We will kill their warlord. The army will scatter once their leader is dead."

"But how?" asked one of the captains. "Our small army cannot defeat such a huge force."

The warlord held up his hand. "Listen to my plan. The tent of the enemy warlord is in the middle of his troops. Our army is small, yes. But if we focus our effort on one goal— getting to the warlord— we will succeed. We will not spread out and try to fight the entire army. Captain, gather your troops into a long column only nine men wide. We will march that line into their midst and head straight for the warlord's tent. That will be our focus."

The soldiers did as they were commanded. They lined up in the column and started marching directly toward the enemy warlord's tent. They held their weapons at the ready, but since their goal was to kill the warlord and no one else, they did not stop to fight. Instead, they quickly and steadily pushed through the enemy ranks. The line was pointed like a spear toward the goal.

The enemy army was caught unaware by this maneuver. No one was trying to engage them in battle! They attacked a few soldiers on the outsides of the column, but were unable to stop the focused and steady movement of the small army toward the warlord's tent. Word got to the warlord that this army was bearing down on him like a magical spear. He panicked and surrendered, giving a tiny army with focus victory over an enemy that was ten times their size.

"Think of your problem in the same way," said the opera master to Wang Zhang Yong. "You need to work on one goal at a time. Center your attention on the routine and nothing else. Take one motion and practice it until you achieve perfection, then move on to the next. Be relentless in your concentration."

"I will try, Master," said Wang Zhang Yong solemnly.

"I know you will. And I will give you something to assist you." The opera master held up a small musical instrument: two cup-like bells connected by a long string. "These are Pengling hand bells. Here, hold them by the string in the middle and tap one against the other."

Wang Zhang Yong tapped the bells together. He heard a gentle chime.

"Use that chime to remind you to concentrate. Decide on your focus and tap the bells when you are ready to work. Find your center, practice well and you will succeed," said the master.

Wang Zhang Yong took his teacher's advice. He focused on one task at a time instead of worrying about several things at once. Using the Pengling bells to help him focus, he mastered the staff routine so well that he was given the lead role of the Monkey King in a famous opera. It was the proudest moment in his mother's life when she saw her son in his first performance.

Wang Zhang Yong married, had children, and spent many years as an acclaimed performer in the opera. He was 45 years old when his mother died and he inherited the responsibility for the family chests. He built a room in his house to accommodate the six chests, including his own, which he called the "Centering chest". When he retired from the opera, he put the Pengling bells in his chest as a reminder of his efforts to achieve focus in his work and in his life.

— Chapter 9 —

Stories of Ten Chests

The Curiosity Chest

The next chest keeper, born in 1753, was Wang Lie Jie. He kept his mother and father quite busy when he was a toddler, because he had a curious mind and was always getting into things. Other children would be content to sit with a puzzle or toy. Wang Lie Jie, however, never sat still. He investigated everything in every room, looking under, through and around things. His favorite playthings were stones and blocks, and he used them to build elaborate fantasy structures that he was always sad to dismantle at the end of the day.

As he grew older and attended school, Wang Lie Jie always asked questions and was never satisfied with a short answer. He had a driving ambition to discover the wonders of the world around him, whether it was through reading books or exploring nearby parks. He left no stone unturned in the quest to feed his imagination and satisfy his curiosity.

Wang Jie Lie was proud to be the oldest child and the future family chest keeper. He explored the treasures in the six chests as often as his parents would let him. He was scolded more than once for spreading the entire contents of one of the chests out on the floor to examine everything more closely! Wang Jie Lie built his own chest, the "Curiosity chest", when he was only thirteen years old. He designed it with rounded corners to be able to hold lots of odd-sized trinkets, and outfitted it with built-in compartments of various sizes. It held many small treasures from his childhood adventures, including stones, coins and little gadgets he had made.

At the age of fifteen, Wang Lie Jie apprenticed himself to a master gardener, and after ten years of work and study became a designer of private gardens. He enjoyed creating landscapes of beautiful spaces and often included secret paths and hidden grottoes in the gardens he designed.

The garden in his own home was a masterpiece of airy pavilions, beautiful lotus ponds, and unique rock formations. As a visitor walked the winding paths, he came upon scene after charming scene, culminating in a beautiful rock garden. At the center of the rock garden was a limestone rock that was taller than most men and as wide as three doors. It had many strange shapes and holes. This type of rock was called a scholar's stone, and was a prized item to have in any garden. Wang Lie Jie was proud of his scholar's stone, and had used drills and files to enhance the shapes and holes, making it truly unique. He even created a miniature version of the large stone that he kept in his Curiosity chest. It reminded him of the way his mind worked: always flowing from idea to idea, always curious to find what was around the next bend.

When Wang Lie Jie married at age thirty, the garden was a favorite place for him and his wife to walk and relax. It was also a favorite place for their children to run and play. Wang Lie Jie's oldest child, born in 1787, was a bright little girl named Wang Liu Yang. One sunny afternoon when she was six years old, she was playing with her younger brother in the garden while her parents were enjoying tea in one of the pavilions. Suddenly, Wang Lie Jie heard his daughter crying as she ran up the path to the pavilion.

"Father! Mother! He's gone! I can't find him anywhere," she called.

"What?" asked her mother. "Your brother is missing?"

"No, Mother," answered the little girl. "Not him. My turtle! I set him down on the path and turned away for a minute. When I looked back, he was gone."

"People think that turtles move slowly, but that is not correct," said Wang Lie Jie. "This is something new you have learned today."

"I learned it too late, Father. How will I ever find my little turtle in the garden?" she sighed.

"Come, Daughter," said Wang Lie Jie as he stood up. "We will look for your turtle and we will leave no stone unturned!"

Father and daughter, assisted by her little brother, began their search for the turtle. They went back to the spot on the path where Wang Liu Yang had set the turtle down. The ground cover on each side of the path was green and lush. A turtle could easily hide and be lost in it.

"Now look carefully," instructed Wang Lie Jie. "Crouch down and part the leaves. Your turtle may not have gotten very far. He could have stopped to eat lunch."

They spent several minutes searching for the turtle, father on one side of the path and daughter on the other, but it was no use. The turtle seemed to have disappeared. The little girl stood up and stretched. "My back hurts, Father," she complained. "And where is Little Brother?"

Her brother called out from further down the path. "I am here. I am turning over stones by this fountain. That's what father always says to do; be a curious stone turner! Right, Father?"

Wang Liu Yang ran to the fountain, scolding her brother. "Father has laid those rocks in a pattern, and you are disturbing it!"

Wang Lie Jie was close behind. "It is all right, Daughter," he reassured her. "The stones can be replaced. Little Brother has the right idea."

"Here's a stone that is darker than the rest, father," said the little boy. "I wonder what it can be." He picked up the stone and it squirmed in his hand. "It's alive!" he squealed.

"Oh!" said Wang Liu Yang as she reached for it. "It's my turtle! Thank you, Little Brother. You found him!"

"The turtle must have been looking for water," said Wang Lie Jie. "Let's let him drink for a moment and then go tell your mother he has been found. And keep turning stones, my children. You never know what you may find."

The Challenge Chest

Wang Liu Yang, the little girl who lost her turtle, was the first child of Wang Lie Jie and would eventually become the keeper of eight family chests, counting her own. She loved most animals, especially small ones such as turtles, but did not feel the same way about larger animals. She was afraid of anything bigger than the family's small terrier dog.

During an especially hot summer in the city, when Wang Liu Yang was nine years old, her parents sent her and her little brother to visit their uncle's home in the country outside Beijing, The uncle was an elephant trainer. Wang Liu Yang's brother was excited to go. He loved being around the elephants, and spent all day outdoors with his uncle. Wang Liu Yang was content to stay indoors, reading, crocheting and helping her aunt with household chores. Her uncle offered to show her how to feed and bathe the elephants and teach her elephant training commands such as her brother was learning, but Wang Liu Yang politely declined. Truth be told, she was terrified of the huge elephants.

Her aunt noticed her sitting and staring out the window one afternoon after all the chores were done. "Why not play outside, Little Niece?" she asked.

"I can't. I have to walk past the elephant pen. I'm afraid of the elephants, Auntie," the little girl confessed.

"Ah, I see. I was afraid of the elephants too, when I married your uncle. But it was so tedious to sit inside the house all day while he was outdoors. I finally got up enough courage to get close to the elephants, and I overcame my fear. Your uncle knows what he is doing. He is a good trainer."

"But they are just so big, Auntie. I am afraid one of them will step on me or hit me with his trunk."

"Now, now, Little Niece." Her aunt chided the little girl, but gently. "Do you think Uncle would allow you to get hurt? His elephants are well-trained. He will show you how to behave around them so that you are safe. Come, you do not have to get very close to them at first. Walk with me to the elephant pen. We will stand outside and see if you can overcome your fear." She held out her hand to the little girl.

Wang Liu Yang hesitated. She was comfortable inside the house, playing quietly and helping her aunt. Why should she change anything? Why would she deliberately get close to a terrifying elephant? Taking risks did not come naturally to her. She supposed her aunt would let her stay in the house if she really wanted to. But did she really want to? Of course she trusted her uncle to keep her safe. Maybe this was a risk worth taking. Perhaps she could push herself out of the comfortable house to go outside, play with the other children and maybe, just maybe, touch an elephant's trunk.

the calligraphy would say they had never seen more beautiful characters or ones that expressed emotion so eloquently.

One morning, in 1855 when he was fifty years old and an established calligrapher, Wú Li Ming was arranging his brush and ink tools. He had just put some water on the ink stone when a neighbor arrived unexpectedly. Wú Li Ming offered his friend tea. As they sat down, he absentmindedly picked up his ink stick and began to rub it on the stone. His friend was having trouble in his business and wanted to talk about his worries. While he listened, Wú Li Ming picked up his brush and began to write, hardly noticing what he was doing. After a few minutes the neighbor interrupted his story and asked Wú Li Ming, "What have you got there?"

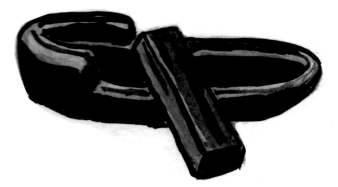

"What? Oh," Wú Li Ming chuckled. "I seem to have written a word while you were talking. I apologize."

"Let me see," his friend said as he turned the paper around. The word "decision" 决定 was written on the page in a strong calligraphy script. "Why did you write that?"

"I'm not really sure," admitted Wú Li Ming. "I was thinking about what you were saying and wishing I could give you advice."

"Look at the word," said his friend, pointing to the paper. "I think you did give me advice. I need to make some decisions about the men who work for me. I know what standards I have for my business but I haven't made the decision to follow through and hold my workers to those standards. I think you've given me the word I need. May I take this?"

"Of course," said Wú Li Ming, handing him the paper. "I'm very glad that I could help you, even though it was a happy accident."

"I don't think it was an accident," said his friend. "There is an energy that moves from your spirit through your hand onto the paper. It is a gift. You should try it again." He smiled as he bowed and turned toward the door. "Thank you," he called, waving the paper as he left.

Hearing the friend leave, Wú Li Ming's wife came into the room. "What was that all about?" she asked her husband.

"Something rather strange," he answered. "Dear Wife, will you sit down? Humor me for a moment, please." Wú Li Ming got out a fresh sheet of paper and rubbed more ink on his ink stone. "Now talk to me."

"What? What about?"

Wú Li Ming thought for a moment. "Something that is on your mind right now. Something that concerns you."

His wife regarded him with narrowed eyes. "Is anything wrong, Husband? Are you trying to tell me something?"

"No, no, nothing's wrong," he quickly reassured her. "I started writing while our neighbor was talking and the results surprised us both. I want to see if I can do it again, that's all."

"All right." She began to speak, and after a few moments of listening, he began to write. "Well, for one thing, I am glad to be sitting down," she said. "My feet are sore and I am worn out from cleaning. The children are not behaving and the fruits I got from the market today are not ripe. Oh, and I need to make some special tea for your mother. She has a cough again." The tired woman looked up. "Well? Is that enough, Husband?"

— Chapter 10 —

Stories of Ten Chests

The Chest of Words

A baby named Wu Wang Xiu Lan was born to Wu Li Ming and his wife in 1844, the year of the dragon. As a young girl she liked to read, but she didn't hide in the house with her books. She also loved to run and play in the woods and beside the streams, imagining fanciful tales which she would tell to her friends. They spent many sunny afternoons outdoors acting out Wu Wang Xiu Lan's plays, and rainy afternoons indoors telling ghost stories. Wu Wang Xiu Lan could write as well as read, and had begun writing down her stories when she was a young girl. She often asked her father to read them. Many of her early stories did not survive his critiques, but as she matured, her writing did, too.

When it came time for her to inherit the family chests, Wu Wang Xiu Lan would be the keeper of ten, counting her own. Her chest, which her father had built when she twelve years old, was made to look like a stack of books. She called it the "Chest of Words". It had a secret compartment in the lid to hide her most private stories. She would be almost fifty years old before she became responsible for the family chests, but she took the responsibility seriously all her life. As a young married woman in her mid-twenties, she visited her parents' home often, and many times sat with her father in the family shrine room where the chests were kept. They shared stories and memories as well as hopes and dreams. She was proud of the fact that she was one of the female chest keepers and was

"Lan Lan!" they called. "What are you doing? We haven't seen you in ages! Come out and talk to us." The three friends still used the nicknames they had given each other as schoolgirls.

"I've been writing, you sillies," said Wu Wang Xiu Lan amiably as she came outside to walk with her friends in the garden. "My father needs one more story to complete the collection before he takes it to the publisher."

"How exciting, Lan Lan!" said Ning Ning. Su Su crossed her arms and managed a tight smile.

"It's funny to hear my nickname," laughed Wu Wang Xiu Lan. That's part of the pen name that my father made up for me: Lánhuā Bǐ."

"It's cute," said Ning Ning. "I approve."

Su Su frowned. "Isn't your husband mad about you writing? Mine would be."

Wu Wang Xiu Lan shook her head. "No. He's happy for me. Aren't you, Su Su?"

Su Su seemed to be annoyed. "Oh, of course I am. How could you say such a thing? I don't like to read, but I guess it's all right for some people." She sighed. "I'm thirsty. Have you had tea yet?"

The young women went into the house for tea. Ning Ning kept up the conversation, asking about the stories in the book and when it would be published. A cup of tea didn't help Su Su's disposition. She frowned and said, "If you were not spending all your time writing stories, you could make better tea cakes." Ning Ning rolled her eyes and tried not to laugh, but Wu Wang Xiu Lan was stung by the comment. Maybe she was neglecting her duties at home. She asked her husband about it that night.

"No, don't think that," he said. "I am proud of your writing. And your friend is wrong. Your tea cakes are fine. In fact, I'd like one right now."

Wu Wang Xiu Lan gave her husband a quick kiss as she jumped up to get him a cake. I guess Su Su just finds fault in everything, she thought with a sigh. That's the way she always is.

A few weeks later, the book had gone to print and Wu Wang Xiu Lan was able to relax a bit. Ning Ning came over for a visit. The two friends took a walk in the garden.

"Why is Su Su not with you?" asked Wu Wang Xiu Lan.

"She is preparing food for her mother-in-law's birthday. She said to tell you she will try to come by later."

Wu Wang Xiu Lan realized what a pleasant time she was having with Ning Ning, without Su Su's negative comments to spoil the conversation.

"I do not like to admit it, but it's much nicer visiting with just you and not Su Su," she said. "She is so mean-spirited. She never has anything good to say."

"I agree," said Ning Ning as the young women came back into the house. "She seems to be jealous of your success and happiness."

Wu Wang Xiu Lan stopped to adjust her hair in the front hall mirror. Suddenly she saw a distant figure reflected in the mirror, shuffling down the path toward the house. She gasped in fright and quickly turned.

"What is it?" asked Ning Ning.

Wu Wang Xiu Lan laughed in relief. "Oh, it's just Su Su coming down the walk. I saw her reflection in the mirror and for a moment I was back in one of my Jiangshi stories."

"So you're saying that Su Su is a vampire?" giggled Ning Ning. "Then quick, hold the mirror up to her face. Jiangshi flee when they see their reflection!"

Both young women laughed for a moment, and then Wu Wang Xiu Lan became more serious. "I don't want to laugh at Su Su," she said. "But in a way, she is a vampire."

However, Chen Wang Ping now had the chance for the first time to really observe his family. His children were lively youngsters, and he enjoyed watching them play and help their mother. But something was wrong. Even though he was right there in the room, his children hardly interacted with him. When they needed something, they asked their mother. When they came in the house with a flower or a little turtle to show, they went straight to their mother.

Chen Wang Ping realized his children did not know him. They knew he was their father, of course, but they had no real relationship. He slumped on the couch and watched a world spin around him that he was not part of. What was he making money for? he wondered. What was the end goal? Where was the heaven he was reaching for? Had he missed it all along, and it was right here on earth, right here in this house? Work had been everything to him. He had tried to be strong when under pressure, but he had forgotten that the reason bamboo does not break is because it bends. Chen Wang Ping decided to bend, and change. It was time to make his family a priority. He wanted to know his children, now, before it was too late.

As the weeks went by and he began to get stronger, he tried to engage his children in activities. One day when he was able to walk around the house, he offered to fly a kite with his oldest son, Chen Lu Wei.

The boy said, "Father, you don't have to play with me. My brother can help me fly the kite."

"No," said Chen Wang Ping. "I want to fly the kite with you. I really do, my son. Get Younger Brother and we'll both help you." The kite flew well and Chen Wang Ping was happy to see how his sons worked together while flying it.

Slowly over the next few weeks, Chen Wang Ping got to know his children. He told them stories, took walks with them, and played with them. It turned out to be the most wonderful time of his life. His wife was thrilled. She had been feeling neglected, too. Now she saw an attentive and fun-loving side to her husband she had not seen in years. Their relationship blossomed anew, and she felt like she was falling in love again.

One evening after dinner as the children were getting ready for bed, Chen Wang Ping saw his youngest daughter playing with a little bamboo flute. She tried to blow a few notes through it, lost interest, and ran off to join her sister, dropping the flute on the floor.

Chen Wang Ping's mind was flooded with memories as he picked up the flute. He wondered if he could remember any of the tunes he used to play. He held up the flute and tried to play a few notes. The sounds of a sweet lullaby instantly came to his fingers, as if he had just played them yesterday.

Meanwhile, his wife was struggling to get the children in bed. Hearing her scolding them, Chen Wang Ping spoke up. "Children! Do as your mother says. If you will all get in your beds quickly, I will send a beautiful bird to sing to you."

"A beautiful bird, Father?" his son Chen Liu Wei asked. "Where is it?"

"You cannot see it," his father answered. "But you will be able to hear it if you lay quietly in your beds."

The children quickly settled down and Chen Wang Ping's wife came out of the bedroom with a questioning look on her face. He motioned for her to come and sit by him and he lifted the flute to his lips. The lullaby's sweet melody emerged, pure and true. The children whispered and giggled in delight.

"Now be quiet," their mother warned. "Go to bed obediently every night, and you will be able to hear the beautiful bird. It will play until you fall asleep."

"I know," his father answered. "But was that really a sword worth dying on? Pick your battles, my son. People will admire you for being forgiving and gracious and not always fighting."

"I don't think I should forgive someone who was unfair to me," said Chen Mogwai.

Chen Liu Wei shook his head sadly. "Then you will carry that anger with you the rest of your life. It will hurt you more than it punishes the other person. Please think about it, my son."

Chen Mogwai stood and bowed. "Thank you, Father. I will try."

But Chen Mogwai did not change. His mistrust and anger ruled him, and his life was bitter and unhappy. It distressed Chen Cheng Gong to see his brother so dissatisfied. His conversations with Chen Mogwai were no more fruitful than their father's had been. Eventually, the brothers stopped talking to each other.

Chen Cheng Gong moved to Thailand with his wife and children to work for a company that built handmade rosewood furniture. It was in Thailand that he built his own chest. The chest was made of sumptuous rosewood with brass details and painted flowers. He called it the "Abundance chest". Chen Cheng Gong wanted a life of abundance. He knew that if he embraced the yin and the yang of life as his father had taught him, and was open to giving and receiving as opportunities came, that he would have that abundant life. He would fill his chest with fond hopes and treasured memories.

After their father died in 1975 and Chen Cheng Gong became the keeper of the twelve family chests, he received a phone call from his brother. Chen Mogwai was resentful that Chen Cheng Gong was in possession of all the chests. He thought it was unfair that the oldest child should automatically be the family chest keeper. He told his brother, "Our grandfather promised to give me his jade ring and our grandmother's ivory fan. They are in his Bamboo chest. I will be in Thailand on business next month and will come to get them."

"All right," said Chen Cheng Gong. "It will be good to see you." He didn't mind giving his brother the items that were promised to him by their grandfather. The family chests were overflowing with treasures and he was happy to see others appreciate them. He just wished that Chen Mogwai could take the keepsakes with a spirit of goodwill instead of entitlement.

Chen Cheng Gong went into the special room where he kept the family chests. He took the ring and the fan from the Bamboo chest and wrote a note saying that those items were being given to Chen Mogwai. After he put the note in the chest and closed the lid, he had a thought. It might be a good idea to keep track of the items in all the chests. Yes, he would make that his next weekend project: an inventory list for each chest. It would take some time, but it would be worth it for future generations. It would also be a way to note items that were given away, such as the fan and ring that were going to his brother.

The very next morning, Chen Cheng Gong entered the family chest room armed with a yellow legal pad and several sharpened pencils. He decided to start the inventory at the beginning, with the oldest and most precious chest: the original Dynasty chest that had belonged to Marco Polo. He had heard stories about Marco Polo and his Sherpa guide since he was a boy, and was very proud of the legacy and history contained in the Dynasty chest.

He sat down, opened the chest and began to remove the contents. It took all morning to examine each item carefully and write its description on the legal pad, but it was fascinating work. There were chopsticks, charms, coins and paper money, jewelry and loose stones, daggers, compasses, tea sets, jade and wood figurines and toys, paintings and poetry, and of course the golden paiza from Kublai Khan. When he was done, he would have the list typewritten and copied. After taking out and writing down the last treasure, a box of whistling arrowheads, Chen Cheng Gong stood and stretched. One chest down, twelve to go. He figured he would repack the Dynasty chest and take a break for lunch.

But what was this? Looking down into the empty chest from his standing position, Chen Cheng Gong noticed something odd. The wood of the bottom wasn't the same color as the interior sides. It was much lighter, and wasn't finished. Strange. He knelt back down and felt the inside of the chest, both the bottom and the sides. They were indeed made from different types of wood. Being a man who dealt in furniture for a living, this intrigued Chen Cheng Gong. He got down on his hands and knees and examined the outside of the chest, then the inside. His trained eyes noticed another oddity: the interior floor of the Dynasty chest didn't seem to be as deep as it looked from the outside, by about an inch. This could mean only one thing, he thought excitedly. A false bottom! He carefully tilted the old chest up on two of the claw feet and gently wiggled it until the false bottom shifted enough for him to wedge a pencil in the narrow opening and ease the panel out.

This was incredible! He had found a secret compartment in the ancient Dynasty chest! Chen Cheng Gong laid the panel aside and eagerly looked to see what had been hidden under it. There was only one thing: a small rolled-up parchment. He picked it up. No, it was leather, tied with a leather cord. Taking it to a table, he gingerly untied the cord and spread the leather out. What was this? A secret letter from a lover? Maybe a will? He looked closer. The leather had Chinese characters on it, and also drawings. He couldn't read all the characters, but he understood some of them. It was a map.

Shaking his head in wonder, Chen Cheng Gong carefully rolled the map up again. He wanted to show this treasure to his wife. After lunch, they could examine it together. She was skilled at reading traditional Chinese. Maybe together they could decipher exactly what the map was for.

It took several sessions of study to thoroughly read the map. Chen Cheng Gong's wife worked on deciphering it while Chen Cheng Gong completed the inventory of the family chests. He decided to give a copy of the inventory to his brother Chen Mogwai, to prevent any arguments in the future about what treasures the chests held.

"I think I've finally finished it," said Chen Cheng Gong's wife as he came into the kitchen. She was sitting at the table with several reference books and two weeks' worth of notes and scribbles almost covering up the map.

"Wonderful," said Chen Cheng Gong. "Is it what we thought? A treasure map?"

"Yes, I'm sure of it," she said. "It says that there are fifty gold coins buried inside the Great Wall of China, and tells exactly the location on the Wall to dig for them! Isn't that amazing?"

Chen Cheng Gong pulled a chair up to the table and examined the map. "It certainly is. I wonder if the coins were really buried there. The map was hidden, so it was very important to someone."

"I wonder who hid it. And who was it hidden from?" his wife asked.

"We'll never know. The coins may have been found centuries ago. The map looks to be that old. Honestly, it may not have been real at all. Maybe it was a party game, or an illustration for a story."

"True. I suppose it will always be a mystery," Chen Cheng Gong's wife said as she began to clear the papers off the table. The novelty of the map wore off within a few days, and it was added to the inventory and put safely back in the Dynasty chest.

The following week, Chen Mogwai came for the fan and ring. The visit went as Chen Cheng Gong had imagined. Even though the family greeted Chen Mogwai with kindness, he was abrasive and unfriendly. "It's unfair. Just because you are the older son, you get to be the keeper of all these treasures. Why don't I get anything?" he complained.

Chen Cheng Gong tried to explain. "They don't belong to me, but to our entire family. I have the responsibility of keeping the chests safe and seeing that they are a benefit to all of us, since they contain life lessons we can learn from. There are plenty of treasures, both material and spiritual, that are contained in the family chests. We don't need to be miserly with them. Giving creates more abundance."

Chen Mogwai was dismissive of this philosophy. "Oh, such high words. Some of the treasures are very valuable and you just want them for yourself!"

Chen Cheng Gong sighed. "Take this," he said, handing his brother a large envelope. "I did an inventory of all the chests. Everything is listed. I would not be dishonest with you."

"So you say," said Chen Mogwai. He pulled out the first page and began to read it. "Hmm. There are many valuable things in the Dynasty chest. And what's this? I don't remember our father showing us a treasure map!"

"I only recently found it, when I discovered the chest had a false bottom. Come, let me show it to you."

The brothers examined the map together, and the prospect of finding fifty ancient gold coins made Chen Mogwai practically drool with greed. "What if it's real? We would be so rich if we had these coins!" he said.

"Be realistic. It's very unlikely," said Chen Cheng Gong. "Besides, anyone who tried to dig a hole in the Great Wall of China would be arrested."

"Maybe so," his brother agreed. "But I still think it's unfair that you get to keep all these treasures. I'll take these things grandfather gave me and make my own chest. Why shouldn't I have one too?"

"My brother," said Chen Cheng Gong. "Our family tradition says that the oldest child is the keeper of the family chests, and builds his own chest as well. But that doesn't mean that no one else can have one. You and I are living in different countries now. It would be a good idea for you to start your own tradition. Make a chest for yourself and pass it on to your children. Put your memories and your life lessons into it so your descendants may learn from you."

"Oh, I will fill my own Dynasty chest," snorted Chen Mogwai. "But I'm going to fill it with gold and jade and things that have real value. Not your stupid life lessons. You can keep those." And with that, he turned and left.

Chen Cheng Gong sighed as he watched his brother walk angrily away. Everything is still a fight with Chen Mogwai, he thought sadly. What kind of legacy is that to leave to your children? His wife met him in the doorway. "I am sorry your brother causes you grief, Husband," she said. "But come in now. Our son is eager to receive his fifteenth birthday gift. He knows it is his new chest, and he wants to put his latest school paper in it."

Chen Cheng Gong felt his mood lift as he walked back into the house. The true spirit of the Dynasty chest lived on in his family, and it sustained him.

— Chapter 11 —

Kim Yost:

A Modern-Day Marco Polo meets a Dynasty Chest Keeper

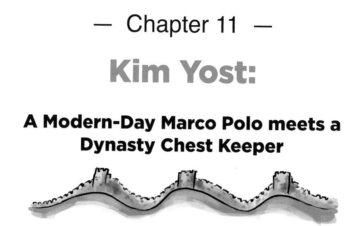

In early March, Leah spent a weekend out of town for her niece's baby shower. Meg and April decided to stay with Josh so he wouldn't be alone. They arrived Friday afternoon after school. As soon as they came into the house, April ran into the dining room. She unpacked some papers from her backpack and spread them out on the table.

"Look at this, Grandpa," she called as Josh followed her. "I'm doing our family tree for a school project. See? I've got a chart that really looks like a tree, and I'm writing everybody's names on it. Here's me and my mom and dad, and above my mom's name is *her* mom and dad." She pointed to a leaf on the tree. "That's you, her dad. See? There's your name."

"Great job, Blossom," said Josh. "I bet you get a good grade on it. And that'll be a nice thing to keep in your life chest, too."

"Yeah. I got some new colored pencils! I can put five different colors of green on the tree. But there's one thing I'm trying to understand, Grandpa," said April, frowning. "How can you be a dad and a grandpa at the same time?"

"We're different things to different people, Blossom," said Josh. Meg came in with a cup of coffee for Josh and hot cocoa for April.

"Thanks, Daughter," said Josh as he took the cup.

"Grandpa!" said April. "She's not Daughter, she's Mom!"

"That's exactly what I mean," laughed Josh. "She's *your* mom, but she's *my* daughter. And she's both those things at the same time. Here. Take a look at your family tree. We have lots of different connections. The leaf above mine is my mom. She's Meg's grandma and your great-grandma. One of the leaves above her is Noah. That's my mom's dad, and my grandpa. His mom was my great-grandma Ashley, and—"

"Maybe that's enough for now," said Meg. "I don't know about April, but my head is starting to spin!" She walked back into the kitchen.

"But I'm just getting to the best one," Josh called after her. "Great-Grandma Ashley's dad was my great-great-grandpa Kim Yost."

"Oh, I've heard you talk about him!" said April.

"I have a lot of great stories about Gramps," said Josh. "He led an incredible life."

Meg came back in with a cup of coffee for herself and sat down at the table. "Okay, let's hear some of those stories. April's done enough work on her family tree for today. Tell us about Great-Great-Grandpa Kim."

"Well, you know he was the one who wrote the *Pumptitude* books. The ones that really changed my life. I read his first two books that summer I was in New York and got to know Bernie." Josh smiled at the memories. "Bernie and I both owe a lot to Gramps. His life story is an inspiration. You've read his books, Meg."

"Yes," nodded Meg. "The summer before I started college. April, you'll read them too someday."

April was full of questions. "What was Great-Great-Grandpa Kim like as a little kid? Did he have brothers and sisters? Where did he go to school?"

"Let your grandpa get started, honey," said Meg. "He'll get to all that."

"I know what we should do," decided Josh. "Let's go into to my study and open up Gramps' life chest. I'll be able to remember the best stories once I start going through the treasures in that chest."

"You've got his life chest here?" asked Meg. "Isn't your cousin Bernie the official life chest keeper for the family?"

"Yeah, but we decided to share it back and forth," answered Josh. "Last time Bernie came to visit, he brought Gramps' life chest with him so I could have it for a while. It's been great looking through the old journals again."

"Good idea. That life chest means a lot to both of you," said Meg. "Finish up your cocoa, April."

April drained the cup and ran. "I love looking through the life chests!" she said. "Oh, wait." April stopped at the study door and counted on her fingers. "He was your great-great-grandpa, so that makes him my mom's great-great-great-grandpa, and my great-great-great-great-grandpa, right?" she asked triumphantly.

"You got it, Blossom," said Josh, patting her on the head while he pushed the button to slide the door open. "But we don't want the story to last all day, so let's just call him Gramps."

They settled themselves in the study. Josh opened the life chest and took out a stack of journals. He also picked up an old photograph. It was a family picture: a mom, a dad, a boy and three girls.

"Here's a good picture to start with. Gramps was born way back in 1954, in Canada. This picture is of his whole family. Here's his mom, his stepdad Papa Tony, and his three little sisters.

From what I understand, he was a pretty unusual kid. He was inventing things and starting businesses even before he was a teenager. Other kids just hung around at home watching TV, but Gramps never sat still. He loved to meet new people and try new things. His first job as a grownup was perfect for doing that. He was a buyer for a department store, and it was really exciting."

April frowned. "Grandpa, how could that job be exciting? It sounds boring."

"Far from it," answered Josh. "The company sent him all over the world. He got to travel and explore, like Marco Polo. Gramps and Marco Polo sort of had the same kind of job. They were both merchants, scouting around for things to sell to people back home. You know, I think life was really one big adventure to Gramps no matter what kind of job he had. Look at this little double-decker bus, Blossom," said Josh as he took a die-cast metal vehicle out of the chest.

"Is that a toy from when Gramps was a little kid?" asked April.

"No, he got this on one of his buying trips. It's the kind of bus they have in London, so he got it as a souvenir. Gramps liked to pick up keepsakes from all the places he traveled. Here's a cork from a bottle of wine that he drank in Italy on that same trip. And some chopsticks from China. He kept these journals too, and wrote down a lot of things that happened on his trips. I'm really glad he did. I learned a lot from his journals."

"Hey," interrupted April. "You told me Marco Polo did that, too. He kept a journal of his adventures!"

"He sure did," agreed Josh. "He and Great-Great-Grandpa Kim had a lot in common." Josh picked up a little elephant made of wood. "I think the best souvenirs Gramps got were from his trip to Bangkok."

"Can I hold the elephant? What's it made of?" asked April.

"Sure. It's made of rosewood," said Josh as he handed it to her. "I remember reading in his journal about the first time he saw a real elephant. It was on that furniture buying trip to Bangkok."

"What's an elephant got to do with furniture?" asked April.

"It has to do with the wood," answered Josh. "Gramps got to ride on one of the elephants that were pulling the rosewood logs out of the forest."

"Oh, I really want to hear this," said Meg. "This was one of my favorite stories when I was your age, April. But I should start supper."

"Let's all help," said Josh. "I need to show you where everything is. Okay, Blossom?"

"Okay, but you'll finish the story after we eat, right?" asked April, rummaging through the life chest. "Hey, here's some funny looking money. Is it Chinese?"

"It's from Thailand," answered Josh, glancing at the coins. "Maybe Gramps got it from the man from Bangkok who showed him the rosewood forest. I'll tell you after supper, Blossom."

The three got up to leave the study. April tossed the coins back into the open life chest. They landed on top of a journal with the words "Bangkok, 1983" handwritten on the cover.

The coins were part of a more complicated story that Josh didn't know. The man from Bangkok was Chen Cheng Gong, and in 1983, the day before he met Kim to take him into the rosewood forest, he had an unexpected visit from his brother, Chen Mogwai.

Chen Cheng Gong welcomed his brother with open arms, but he couldn't help feeling a bit wary. Chen Mogwai always had a motive for his visits, and it usually involved money. They sat down to a cup of tea, and five minutes into their conversation, Chen Cheng Gong proved himself right. Chen Mogwai was his usual self, bitter and suspicious. He could not let go of the idea that he was being cheated somehow by not being in possession of the family chests. "You are older than I, so by tradition, you keep the chests," he said. "So what? Maybe I should have them with me. After all, I am still in China, where our ancestors lived."

"My brother, you know you can trust me," said Chen Cheng Gong. "I have given you an inventory of everything in the family chests." he said. He received only a grunt from Chen Mogwai in response, so he tried a different tactic. "You should bring your children on your next visit and show them the chests. We can tell them about our ancestors. My children enjoy hearing the stories and are inspired by them."

Chen Mogwai grunted again. "Humph. Better yet, I'll take some things back with me for my children." He looked at the inventory list in his hand. "I want the ink stone from the calligraphy chest. I am sure it is very valuable by now."

Chen Cheng Gong stiffened. He knew his brother did not want the items from the family chests in order to share them with his children. He was sure that Chen Mogwai, for all his talk about ancestors, would be quick to sell any costly item from the family chests that he could get his hands on. "Yes, it must be very valuable," he said carefully. "But I'm sorry. The items in the calligraphy set should not be separated. And unless your children are studying calligraphy, there's no reason to give you the whole set." Chen Cheng Gong had called his brother's bluff. He waited for the response.

"All right," said Chen Mogwai, backing down. He stood and started toward the room where the chests were kept. "Let's go have some family time. Pick your favorite chest and tell me all the stories in it." He tried to sound friendly, but Chen Cheng Gong could hear the falseness in his brother's voice. With a sigh, he followed him to the family shrine room.

Once inside, Chen Mogwai headed straight for the Dynasty chest, running his finger along the drawings on the lid. "Let's talk about this one," he said. "I told a friend of mine about that map you found in this chest. He's an antique dealer, and he wants to look at it."

Chen Mogwai opened the chest, digging around for the map. Before he found it, his hand fell on a large black jade dragon figurine. "There are two of these, aren't there?" he said. "I suppose you sold one already and didn't tell me."

"Of course not," said Chen Cheng Gong. "The other one is there. I don't think any of the items should be sold."

"That's easy for you to say," said his brother. "Your business is doing well. I need money, though. So why not sell a few things out of these chests? Like I said, I've got a friend here in Thailand who wants to look at that treasure map. Even if there isn't any treasure, the map itself is valuable. I could get several thousand dollars for it if it's really old."

"I can help you if you need money," said Chen Cheng Gong. "I would much rather do that than sell the treasures from our family chests." He took his money purse from his pocket and started to open it. "How much do you need right now?"

"You think you're so much better than me, don't you?" spat Chen Mogwai. "I don't want your sympathy money!" He smacked the money purse out of his brother's hand and strode angrily toward the door. "I have to go. I'm meeting that friend of mine for dinner. I don't suppose you'll let me have the map? Just to show it to him?"

Chen Cheng Gong spoke quietly but with strength. "No. It pains me to say this, brother, but I do not trust you."

"I will be in town for the rest of the week. You will see me again." Chen Mogwai started to leave and then turned back. "I don't care if you trust me or not. I want my share," he said as he slammed the door behind him.

Chen Cheng Gong picked up his money purse from the floor and closed the Dynasty chest. Was his brother right? Should they start selling off treasures from the family chests? Was it foolish to keep these things when they could bring so much money? No, he decided. That was shortsighted. The family chests contained more than just treasures that could be sold for a price. They represented the lives and the stories of their ancestors. No price could be put on that. Chen Cheng Gong took a set of keys from his pocket and locked the shrine room. There was nothing he could do but keep trying to convince his brother to see the true value of the family chests. But for now he had to put those thoughts aside. Tomorrow was an important work day. He would be meeting Kim Yost, a buyer from Canada who wanted to see the rosewood furniture making process from start to finish.

After hamburgers and pasta salad, Josh, Meg and April returned to the study. Josh paged through the Bangkok journal. "Okay, the elephant story," he said as April settled onto his lap and held the little rosewood elephant. "Gramps was going to meet a man who would take him into the rosewood forest, to see what the furniture was made from. He wanted to see the whole process: cutting the logs in the forest, taking them to the factory, and watching the furniture being made and hand decorated. The person who took him to the forest was a Chinese man named Chen Cheng Gong. Gramps gave everybody nicknames, so he asked the man right away if he could call him Mr. CC."

"You gave me a nickname too, Grandpa," said April. "I like it when you call me Blossom. Did Mr. CC like his nickname?"

"Sure," said Josh. "Gramps was a nice guy. He was friendly to everyone, and Mr. CC liked him and his nickname straight off. So, they drove to the rosewood forest. Gramps had expected to sit through a long car ride. They did that. He expected to tromp around in the woods and watch the logs being cut. They did that. He even expected to see elephants, because he knew they used elephants to pull the logs out of the forest and down the river to the factory. But one thing Gramps hadn't expected was to actually ride an elephant. Can you imagine, Blossom? Two of the elephants had saddles on their backs, tied under their big bellies. One elephant put his trunk down and Mr. CC stood on it. Then the elephant lifted Mr. CC up so he could climb onto the elephant's back. He told Gramps to get on the other elephant! Well, it looked easy, so why not? Mr. CC called for the elephant to put its trunk down and Gramps climbed on. What a feeling it must've been to be raised up into the air on an elephant's trunk!"

"Was he scared?" asked April, her eyes wide.

"Maybe a little," answered Josh. "But he got right up on that elephant anyway. He didn't want to miss the adventure. Being ready for adventure was part of his positive attitude, and Gramps always said that your attitude determines your altitude! Remember reading that, Meg?"

"I sure do," said Meg. "It was in his first book. Looking down from on top of an elephant—what an altitude!"

"What's altitude?" asked April.

"It means how high up you are," explained Josh. "Gramps was probably ten feet in the air on the back of that elephant, Blossom."

"Wow!" she exclaimed. "So where did the elephants take them?"

Kim's elephant ride with Mr. CC

Josh continued the story. "After they were settled in the saddles, the elephants kept on working, dragging their logs out of the forest. Gramps and Mr. CC talked during the ride. Mr. CC said that he had always loved elephants, and that was one of the reasons he moved to Thailand. His whole family loved elephants, and one of his ancestors had been an elephant keeper in the Forbidden City. When they got to the factory with the logs, Gramps and Mr. CC climbed off the elephants the same way they had gotten on, by standing on their trunks. Gramps was so excited that he couldn't stop smiling and thanking Mr. CC for such a great experience. They spent the rest of the day at the factory, seeing how the beautiful hand-carved furniture was made."

"I guess you're right," said April. "His job doesn't sound boring!"

"Not at all," agreed Josh. "And Mr. CC was having just as much fun as Gramps. He enjoyed being around people who loved adventure and embraced life, like Gramps did. So Mr. CC invited Gramps to have dinner at his house that night. It gave them another chance to ride elephants, too. Mr. CC's house was up in the hills and he usually rode an elephant home at the end of the workday. They climbed on again and started off. The elephants lumbered along a lot faster than when they were dragging the heavy logs, and Gramps had a hard time hanging on. When they got to Mr. CC's house, the elephant had decided to poop at the same time Gramps was trying to get off. He slipped backwards and sat down right into a pile of poop!"

"Oh, no! Poor Gramps!" April felt sorry for him even though she was giggling. She held the little rosewood elephant in what she imagined was a 'pooping position'. Meg was laughing too. "Well, an elephant's gotta do what an elephant's gotta do!" she said.

Josh continued the story, taking the rosewood elephant from April in an attempt to quell the giggles. "Mr. CC and Gramps went into the house to meet Mr. CC's family. After they got Gramps cleaned up, they all had a nice dinner together." Josh paused and thought for a second. "You know, Blossom, this was one of Gramps' favorite things to do. He really liked getting to know people in all the different countries he visited."

"That's the best way to learn about a country," said Meg.

"It is," agreed Josh. "Now after dinner, Mr. CC invited Gramps to see the family shrine room. It was nighttime and the room was lit by candles. Gramps saw a collection of wooden boxes in the room, all beautifully made, and all different. Mr. CC told him they were his family's chests. Each one held the keepsakes, stories and memories of one of his ancestors. They went back eleven generations, he said, and the oldest one had originally belonged to Marco Polo. Gramps was fascinated. He knew people kept pictures in scrapbooks and keepsakes in shoeboxes, but he had never seen anything like this. Seeing how interested he was, Mr. CC turned on the electric lights and invited Gramps to sit down and look at the chests. They spent the rest of the evening in the family shrine room. Mr. CC took medals, photos, watches and all sorts of keepsakes from the chests, and told Gramps a story for everything."

"It sounds fascinating," said Meg.

Mr. CC shows Kim generations of family treasures

"I'm sure it was," replied Josh. "Gramps got out the journal that he always kept with him and wrote down a lot of what Mr. CC told him about his ancestors. That's how I know these old Chinese stories, Blossom. Gramps took the time to write them down in his journal."

"I remember, Grandpa," said April. "You told me about all the people who passed down Marco Polo's Dynasty chest. Those were neat stories. I'm glad Gramps wrote them down."

"Me too," said Josh. "I think Gramps' favorite chest was Marco Polo's Dynasty chest. Mr. CC saw how much he liked it, too. He even gave him a couple of things from the chest. Remember the black jade dragon I got from Bernie?"

"I'll get it, Dad," said Meg. She opened Josh's Pirate chest, found the dragon, and handed it to him.

"This dragon is originally from Marco Polo's Dynasty chest, Blossom. There are two of them. Mr. CC gave them to Gramps, and now Bernie and I have them. They make a good reminder of our friendship, because the two of us live so far apart."

"Can I hold it?" asked April. Josh handed it to her. "Whoa. It's really heavy." Meg took the dragon from her hands and carefully set it on an end table. "What else did Mr. CC give him, Grandpa?" asked April.

"An ancient treasure map," answered Josh, looking through the life chest. "Ah, here it is."

"A treasure map?" asked April excitedly. "What kind of treasure? Is it on a deserted island?"

Josh unrolled the map to show them. "It says on the map that the treasure was buried in the Great Wall of China. One of the stories that Mr. CC told Gramps was about this map. Remember the coins Marco Polo got from Kublai Khan, the ones that he and his guide hid in the Dynasty chest?"

"Yup," said April. "That was one of my favorite stories. Is that the treasure?"

"Yes. According to the story that Mr. CC told Gramps, one of the guide's descendants took the coins out of the Dynasty chest, hid them in the Great Wall and made this map to show where they were."

"I wonder why they were hidden," said Meg. "And I wonder why Mr. CC gave the map to Gramps."

"Gramps said in his journal that Mr.CC wasn't able to go back to China to get the coins," said Josh. "Something about a problem with his visa. So he gave the map to Gramps. Gramps said if he ever went to China he would try to find out if the coins were really there, but he didn't get the chance."

"Mr. CC was a nice man, wasn't he?" asked April.

"He was," said Meg. "And he certainly trusted Gramps."

"Great-Great-Grandpa Kim was that kind of guy," said Josh. He held up a picture of a grinning Kim Yost with his arm around Mr. CC. "How could you not trust that face?"

Chen Cheng Gong did trust Kim. He needed someone he could trust; someone who understood the importance of the Dynasty chest and all the family chests that came after it. Although he enjoyed showing Kim the treasures in the chests and explaining the family legacy, he was distracted by worry. Soon, perhaps tomorrow, his brother would be back, demanding to raid the chests. Chen Cheng Gong didn't mind giving Chen Mogwai items for his children, but he knew that anything his brother received would not stay in the family. It would be sold to the highest bidder. And here in this room with him now was a young man from another culture who understood the value of these chests better than his own brother did.

Chen Cheng Gong would do his best to keep Chen Mogwai from destroying the family legacy, but first he would act to make sure at least some of the treasures were in good hands. He looked at Kim, who was writing a final few notes in his journal and glancing around the room with awe. Then his eyes fell upon the two things from the Dynasty chest his brother had coveted most: the treasure map and the black jade dragons. Impulsively, he picked them up in one swoop and thrust them into Kim's arms. "I would like you to have these," he said. "You have shown such interest in our culture and you have been— how do they say it? A good sport. Because of the elephants."

"Oh, well. Poop happens," laughed Kim. "The jade dragons are beautiful. Thank you, Mr. CC. But this map—do you think it's real? And if it is, don't you want to go to China yourself to find the coins?"

"I am not able to travel back to China," said Mr. CC. "My visa has been held up for quite some time." He hesitated, and then spoke again. "There is no one else in my family who could undertake such a risky job. You are young, and ambitious. If the opportunity ever presents itself, I trust you to find the coins for me and my family."

"All right," said Kim. "Thank you again. I'll keep in touch. If I ever get a chance to go to China and dig around the Great Wall, I'll let you know. If I find the gold coins, I'll get them to you."

Mr. CC smiled at the honest, straightforward young man who had so quickly become his friend. He was making the right choice. "My thanks go to you as well," he said. "But who knows? The whole story may be fiction. Fifty gold coins made by Kublai Khan's goldsmith? Hidden in the Dynasty chest and then buried in the Great Wall? Some of my ancestors were professional storytellers, you know."

"You're a pretty good storyteller yourself, Mr. CC," said Kim. He turned to open the door, but his hands were full. "I'm going to need something to put all these souvenirs in," he said.

"You need your own chest," said Mr. CC, opening the door for him. "I have a beautiful one I can show you at the factory tomorrow before you leave." His eyes fell on a few coins in the corner of the room where they had fallen from his money purse. "Here, take these coins. You told me you collect money from every country you visit."

"Thanks again, for everything." Kim grinned as he put the coins in his pocket. "This trip has been really special."

After that first trip to Asia, Kim Yost flew home with many ideas for the furniture business, but with much more. He had the memories of unforgettable experiences, the joy of new friends, lots of wonderful souvenirs, a hand carved rosewood chest in which to store his souvenirs, and an idea that would change lives.

— Chapter 12 —

Creating the Life Chest and Building the Legacy

April spent most of the next morning making videos with her comm. She ran around the house taping Josh and her mom and asking them to hold the comm while she sang songs and did cartwheels.

"When I get home, I'm gonna upload these vids to my life chest, Grandpa," she said excitedly. The built-in digiscreen is really neat!"

"You sure you want to keep them all?" asked Josh, laughing. "Even the one where you tried to do a headstand and fell over? Meg, maybe you better look through her player and delete some of those vids."

"Are you kidding?" said Meg, as April danced by with a flashing hula hoop. "I'm saving all of them. They're going to play on an endless loop at her high school graduation party."

"Well, if I look silly, please edit me out," said Josh, shaking his head.

"You and me both, Dad," agreed Meg.

April's energy eventually subsided a bit. After lunch they sat in the study again to hear more stories from Josh.

"I'm glad you have so much fun making videos for your life chest, Blossom," said Josh. "You know, it's because of my great-great-grandpa Kim that we all have our life chests."

"He came up with the idea, didn't he?" asked Meg.

"Yes, right after that trip to Thailand I was telling you about. He was so inspired, meeting Mr. CC, seeing his family chests and hearing all the stories. He saw how the idea of those chests could be used to hold memories, sure. But also to inspire people to live their best lives in the here and now, and plan how they want their lives to be in the future. Gramps didn't sleep much on the plane ride back to Canada from Thailand. His head was full of memories from his trip, but also a new idea: to start a company to build and sell life chests. Look at this, Blossom." Josh rummaged around a bit in Gramps' life chest until he found what he was looking for.

"This sure is an old piece of paper," said April. "There's lots of words on it and a bunch of drawings, too."

"That's how Gramps used to write down his thoughts," said Josh. "He was good at drawing pictures, and when he had an idea he made what he called a mind map. This is the original mind map of his life chest idea."

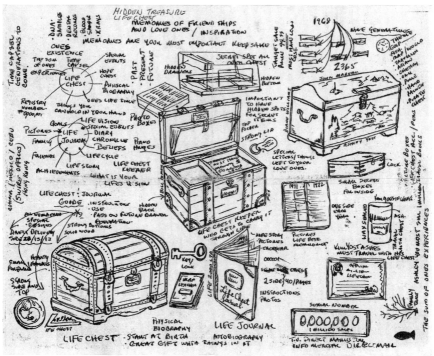

The life chest mind map

"So would you call that thinking outside the box or inside the box?" joked Meg.

"Both!" laughed Josh. "He thought outside the box so people wouldn't have to keep their treasures in a shoe box!"

"I like that he decided to call them life chests," said Meg, looking over April's shoulder at the mind map. "They're not just for memories of our past. They're about our lives right now. I was looking at a video in my life chest player the other day. It was me and some old college friends, and I realized I hadn't taken the time to keep in touch with them as much as I wanted to. That got me on the comm that same afternoon. We made a promise to talk at least once a month."

"Good for you, Meg," said Josh. "I think that's what Gramps had in mind—you know, using our life chests not just to store memories, but to help us connect with the people that matter to us."

April piped up. "Did your Gramps go home to Canada and start making life chests in his garage or something? Or did he sell them on TV?"

Josh laughed. "Well, neither, Blossom. He didn't start the business right away. He was raising his daughter Ashley on his own and starting a new job at another furniture company. He did make a life chest for Ashley when she was a baby, though. They went on a lot of trips together and made great memories to fill their life chests. And he hung onto the mind map and the dream it represented."

As Josh put the mind map back in the life chest, something else caught his eye. He picked up a small handmade book and laughed. "This is the sleeping book," he said as he picked it up to show Meg and April. "Gramps and his boss, Bill Comrie, were on a business trip to Asia, in 1990. There was a lot to do on this trip. Gramps wrote in his journal that they went to seven countries, visited over forty factories, and stayed in more than eleven hotels in two weeks!"

"Wow. So what's the sleeping book?" asked April.

"Here, take a look at it," said Josh. "It's all pictures of Gramps."

"He's sleeping in all these pictures!" exclaimed April.

"Like I said, it was a really busy trip and there wasn't much time to sleep," said Josh. "They traveled around in cars, planes, boats, trains and ferries, and Gramps slept in all of them. He took a power nap whenever he could. His boss took the pictures and put them all in this book as a joke. Gramps was a hard worker and his boss appreciated that. That's what made all the nap pictures so funny."

"He does look funny," giggled April.

"I think taking power naps is a good idea," said Meg. "Then you're fresh and ready for the next adventure!"

"Gramps did have a lot of adventures," agreed Josh. He picked up and paged though another journal. "One night on that same trip, Gramps kept thinking about his life chest idea. It had been about seven years since he had first met Mr. CC in Bangkok. He got the idea to build his own life chest business then, but he hadn't actually made it happen yet. He thought it was about time he did, and Bill Comrie, his boss, really encouraged him. They were done looking at factories for the day, so Gramps figured as long as they were in China, he should try to find a factory to build his life chests. Even though it was midnight, his boss decided to go with him. So there they were, scoping out factories in the middle of the night, with Gramps getting his boss almost as excited as he was about building life chests. Bill loved the idea so much that he became a partner in the business and they built and sold life chests for several years. Gramps was really happy that he was not just dreaming about making life chests, but finally doing it."

"You said he built life chests for several years. Did they stop making them?" asked Meg.

Kim and Bill begin Life 2000

"For a while. Gramps got promoted to CEO and President of the furniture company, and he was so busy with his job that he wasn't able to keep up the life chest business. But the idea didn't go away. His boss, Bill, had something to do with that, too. He gave his half of the life chest company to Gramps' daughter Ashley as a gift. He also set Gramps up on a blind date."

"A blind date? What does that have to do with the life chests, Grandpa?" asked April.

"You'll see, Blossom. Meg, did you ever go on a blind date?"

"Never. Anybody who would do that is more adventurous than I am."

"Gramps was adventurous, wasn't he?" asked April, bouncing up and down in her chair. "Was the blind date an adventure? Wait, Grandpa. What's a blind date?"

"It's when you agree to go out with someone you've never met before, April," answered her mom. "Sometimes a friend sets it up for you, like Gramps' boss set up this date. Like I said, I'd

Donna storms the factory gates

Josh put the citizenship papers back in the life chest and noticed a photo. "Take a look at this," he said, handing it to Meg. "This is Donna in a promotional picture for Life 2000."

Meg studied the photo. "Donna's wearing high-heeled shoes in every picture I've seen of her. She must have had quite a collection. Look, April." She handed the photo to her daughter.

"Oooh," sighed April in admiration. "I want a pair of red ones like that when I grow up!"

"She may have worn high heels, but she didn't teeter around in them," said Josh. "Donna walked with purpose!"

Now it was Meg rummaging through Gramps' life chest. "I just remembered something else," she said. "Do you think Gramps kept copies of his books in his life chest?"

She explained to her daughter, "Gramps wrote some great books, April. Yeah, here's the first one, see? It's called Pumptitude." She handed the book to Josh.

"What's the book about?" asked April.

"Gramps told a lot of stories in his books," answered Josh. "Stories about his life and things he learned along the way. Some of his coworkers and people he admired told their stories, too. Gramps wanted his books to show people how to make a great life."

"You learned a lot from the advice in his books, didn't you, Dad?" remarked Meg.

"That's an understatement. There were so many things I read in his books that have stayed with me all my life. Advice isn't really the right word, though, Meg. He called them learnings. I guess he coined that term because you can't just be taught something and have it change you. You have to choose to learn."

Looking in the life chest again, Meg pulled out another book. "Here's the one that's really special. Magical, even. Right, Dad?"

"You must have found a copy of Maximum Pumptitude!" said Josh. "That was Gramps' second book, Blossom."

"Why did Mom say it was magic?" asked April.

"There's a story in it about a couple of cousins, and—well, it's a pretty complicated story, Blossom. I'm not sure you'd understand it yet. I'll read it to you someday."

"Aw, Grandpa," said April. "It sounds like a good story."

"It is," said Meg. "But we've been in here all afternoon. Aren't you two hungry?"

"Tell you what," said Josh, putting the books back in the life chest. "I'll take you girls out to eat." He picked up a pair of chopsticks from the chest. "How about Chinese?"

April jumped up, excited. "Ooh, yes! I want to practice using chopsticks!"

"Try these right now," said Josh, handing them to her. He turned to Meg. "I remember one more story about Gramps. He used to say that he must've been Chinese in another life, because he was able to use chopsticks perfectly the first time he ever picked them up."

Meg laughed. "Maybe he knew Marco Polo in China, in that other life," she said.

Josh laughed too. "No, he probably was Marco Polo."

"Grandpa, they keep slipping," complained April, trying to keep the chopsticks in one hand.

"Well, let's put those back and get to the restaurant. You can practice there," said Josh.

April set the chopsticks back in the life chest and carefully closed the lid. The three left Josh's study, happily discussing Chinese food and chopstick techniques. The lights in the room dimmed on the little rosewood elephant figurine, still sitting on the end table next to Josh's chair, ready to bring back more memories and inspire more adventures.

Josh only had Gramps' life chest with him on that afternoon of storytelling, but there were many more memories and adventures recorded in the life chests that belonged to the next generations. Kim's daughter Ashley began to fill her life chest when she was a little girl. Report cards, sports keepsakes, and photographs from trips with her father filled the chest in her early years, later giving way to college diplomas, business reports and a marriage license.

Filling her life chest helped Ashley establish her core values. When she put a keepsake in the chest, it reminded her of what was important in her life and what she wanted her future to look like. She also developed a habit of looking through her life chest and adding things to it once a week, as part of her 'Schmonday'. Schmonday was a concept her dad had taught her. It was simple: set aside a chunk of time every week for reflection, learning and planning. His was on Sunday afternoon, but he told Ashley it could be anytime. "Choose your own Schmonday!" Kim reminded his daughter. "Just make sure you have one every week." Ashley did yoga as part of her Schmonday, but she could never talk her dad into it. He preferred his treadmill.

Ashley also learned that she didn't have to limit herself. When she married and began her family, she was determined to embrace the 'power of the AND'. She and her husband worked and planned together so that they could both have satisfying careers and a happy family life raising their son Noah.

Noah's life chest was honey colored wood with brass corners and studded leather straps. Ashley and her husband got it for Noah's first birthday. There were all sorts of presents that Noah was more excited about than his life chest, such as his toy farm set and the stuffed elephant he got from Grandpa Kim. But Ashley knew that in a few years, he would begin to appreciate the value of the life chest, like she did when she was a little girl. It had been so exciting to come home from school with an A+ test or her varsity letter, show it to her dad, and together find the perfect place for it in her life chest. That's what she wanted for Noah, too. She smiled at the thought of the happy days ahead as she watched Noah balance himself on his life chest while he was learning to walk. "Say yes to the chest, little guy!" she told him lovingly.

Ashley kept Noah's life chest in the formal living room, which was normally used only when they had guests. It wasn't that she was afraid Noah would hurt the chest—they were solidly built.

The idea was to keep it special. If it was in his bedroom, it would just turn into another toy chest. He had enough of those, full of blocks, stuffed animals and cars. The life chest was something different, and Noah grew up using it like Ashley did, to mark the special times in his life and inspire him to make a great future.

Ashley encourages Noah to say yes to the chest

He was home from college during winter break of his junior year, in 2037, and sat down with his mom to look through his life chest.

"I sure liked making model cars when I was a kid, didn't I, Mom?" Noah said. "I think I've got three of them in here. Look at this one. I called it my Frankencar. Remember the 3-D printer I built when I was a freshman? I used that for some of the parts and I kit-bashed four other cars to make it."

"It's pretty intense," agreed Ashley. "You've done some wonderfully creative things, Noah."

"Thanks, Mom," said Noah. "You know, looking at these model cars in my life chest is making me think. There are a couple of internships I'm looking at for this summer. One is with a company that designs ceiling fans. That would be okay and it pays well, so I'm thinking I should take it. The other one's a lot riskier. I'm not sure what to do."

"It doesn't sound like you're too excited about ceiling fans, though. Tell me about the other one," said his mom.

"It's with a startup; a new company that's working on a hover car. From what I've heard, they've got some breakthrough technology that's going to really change the industry."

Noah stopped and thoughtfully studied the Frankencar he still held in his hand.

Ashley didn't say anything. She wanted Noah to come to this decision on his own, and he did.

"I think I just answered my own question, Mom," he said. "I want to be involved in creative work. I always have. Just look at this thing!" He gestured with the Frankencar. "It's taking a chance to do an unpaid internship with a startup company. I'll have to take on a night job to pay my bills. But I'm not the kind of guy to spend his life designing ceiling fans. I'm gonna make a great life and it's gonna be on the cutting edge. No regrets. Hey— remember I said that, if I start to complain this summer, okay?"

He stood up, smiling, and handed the Frankencar to Ashley. "I know it's ugly, but don't ever get rid of this. It has to stay in my life chest always." He kissed her on the cheek. "Thanks for the great talk, Mom. Hey, I need to make some calls." He loped out the door. "Later!"

"You're welcome!" Ashley called after him. She smiled as she murmured to herself, "I don't remember saying anything. He did all the talking!"

Noah finalized the plans for his internship at the automotive startup company. He told his grandpa Kim about it that evening, when Ashley called her dad for their regular Sunday night chat.

"It sounds exciting," said Kim. "I'm proud of you. Don't ever settle for less than what you really want. Oh, and one more thing," he added. "Tell those guys not to call them hover cars. It sounds too 20th-century. Call 'em 'levicars' or something."

"Okay, Grandpa," said Noah. "Thanks a lot!"

Noah hung on to the idea about the levicars, but he also remembered what Grandpa Kim had said about never settling for less than what you really want. He lived with Grandpa Kim and Grandma Donna in Michigan that summer, working at his internship in Detroit. While visiting Donna at the Life 2000 office one day, he met Erica, the young woman he would eventually marry. Ashley gave Erica a beautiful white life chest, inset with mirrors and crystals, as a gift at her bridal shower. The couple settled in Michigan, became the parents of two girls, and through the years, filled their life chests with memories, hopes and joys.

The Life Chest Journal

THE
ORIGINAL

Life Chest

Part Four

Past and Present Collide

— Chapter 13 —

The Fable
Becomes a Reality

Noah's daughters, Ruby and Catherine, lived a happy and active childhood. When they visited Grandma Ashley back in Canada, they explored the treasures in her life chest and in their great-grandpa Kim's. Hearing the stories that the keepsakes represented taught them that your life is based on the choices you make. You can choose to live with intention and plan to make a great life. That's what Ruby did. Or you can let life just happen, and make your choices without thinking. That's what Catherine did.

Ruby went to New York for a teaching opportunity, met her husband there, and settled down. As the older daughter, she knew she'd be the life chest keeper for her family one day. She filled her own life chest, proud to know that it would be added to her family's legacy. Filling her life chest helped develop her self-confidence and a sense of her own worth. She got up again after troubles brought her down. She took the lessons from the life chest and used them to make a great life.

Catherine wanted a great life too, but she wasn't clear about how to do it. She moved around a lot as a young woman and never got around to starting her own life chest. While Ruby went to school, established a career, married and started a family, Catherine floundered. An undisciplined life, dead-end jobs, and relationships that were less than healthy dragged her down.

She reached her thirtieth birthday with not much to look back on and little hope for the future. Indianapolis was where she found herself that year. It might as well have been last year in St. Louis or two years before in Cleveland. Another retail job, another dingy apartment, another group of friends as aimless as she was. Except for Ben. She wasn't really looking for a boyfriend, but Ben pursued her, and it was flattering. Exciting, too. He was a bartender, but wanted to be an actor. He was in a few films that were playing on the indie circuit, and an agent in L.A. wanted to sign him.

After a year together, they had saved enough money to move to California. Catherine agreed to work full time while Ben went to auditions. It would be a great adventure, except for one thing. Shortly before the move, Catherine discovered she was pregnant. Impulsively, she decided not to tell Ben about the baby. They hadn't talked about marriage, because the focus had been on Ben's career, but Catherine was sure Ben loved her.

I just want us to get settled in L.A. first, she thought. Maybe even wait till Ben gets a good acting job. In truth, she was terrified that Ben would leave her behind if he found out she was pregnant. They went to California, and Catherine made pretty good money waiting tables. She postponed telling Ben about the pregnancy as long as she could. After they had been in L.A. for more than a month, Catherine finally broke the news. She was starting to show, and was getting more and more tired at work. The conversation didn't go well.

Ben wasn't angry, but he was surprised. And worried. "How can we take care of a baby? We barely make enough to live on with you working full time, and I can't—"

Catherine interrupted. "I don't want you to stop acting. I'm not asking you to."

"I know I haven't gotten many jobs, but I have two auditions coming up that my agent is really excited about. I just can't quit now."

"We can make it work somehow. Can't we, Ben? We talked about having lots of kids someday."

"Yeah, someday. We're just starting sooner than I thought we would."

In 2082 the baby was born, and they struggled along for a while. Catherine had to quit waitressing, but she found a food service job in a day care center, and she was able to take baby Josh with her. Ben got acting jobs here and there, but not the big break they were hoping for. Bills piled up, and life was exhausting. Days went by with Catherine and Ben barely speaking to each other.

Ben didn't act much like a father, either. He left all of Josh's care to Catherine, and took hardly any notice of his son's first steps and first words. Around Josh's third birthday, he began to disappear for a few days at a time. At first he said they were late night shoots, but after a while he didn't bother to make excuses. The night Catherine came home from work and saw the letter from Ben, she wasn't all that surprised. She had suspected this was coming, but she didn't know what she could have done to stop it.

Catherine opened the envelope. She was holding him back, Ben wrote. He needed to be free to travel, to network. He'd never get his big break if he had to worry about her and a kid all the time. It was a mistake to have the baby. He was leaving her. He was sorry.

So was she. Sorry about everything in her life, all the thoughtless choices she'd made and stupid things she'd done. Except Josh. He wasn't a mistake. Catherine crumpled the note in her hand and choked back a sob. She might have given up on life altogether if it hadn't been for her three-year-old son. He was the only thing now that made life worth living, and she would hang on for him. She had to.

Catherine did hang on, doing the best she could to raise Josh on her own, but it was rough for both of them. Ben called a few times over the years, but Josh never knew what to say to him. He didn't know his dad. The only picture he had of him was one his mom had snapped from the TV, that time they saw him as a guest villain on Doctor Who.

Long hours at low-paying jobs meant barely enough money to make ends meet, and very little time for Catherine to spend with her son. Josh was left alone a lot, and started getting into trouble at a young age. As he got older, most of the conversations between him and his mom turned into arguments. They were both going down a path that they didn't know how to change.

What makes the difference between a great life and a not-so-great one? Why do some people just get by and some people thrive? Is it pure luck? Is it intelligence? Other people pulling for you? What control do you even have? Sometimes Josh looked around—at his teachers, at his mom's friends, at celebrities and people in the news, and asked himself those questions. His answer was always the same. Dumb luck, that's what it was. Life's not fair! And those thoughts helped him grow into a bitter, angry young man; a high school dropout and petty criminal by the time he was nineteen.

If Josh could have talked to his aunt and uncle in New York, he would have gotten very different answers to the questions he asked himself. His mom's sister Ruby, her husband Matt and their son Bernie, who was just a year older than Josh, lived a happy and comfortable life in Brooklyn. They were as far away from Josh and his mom in attitude as they were on the map.

"How and where you start out in life is chance, Bernie," said Matt one morning in 2101 as he poured milk on his oatmeal. It was Bernie's twentieth birthday, and his dad felt like giving a bit of a speech. "But the rest of your life is full of choices. Every day you have the chance to make new choices, different than the ones you made yesterday."

"Dad, how do you know what choices to make?" asked Bernie.

"Son, if you know what your passion is, your choices come a lot easier. As you grow up and get to know yourself, you'll find your passion." Matt moved the sugar bowl away from his son's reach. "Whoa, there. Your oatmeal's sweet enough. I hope you find a passion for healthier eating!"

Matt's passion was for his neighborhood and the people in it. He wanted to help make his little corner of the world a better place. He didn't care that most of the people he went to school with wanted high-powered business or law careers. That was okay for them, but his passion was different. He served in the army for three years, and then applied to the police force.

Throughout Bernie's childhood, he saw his dad's passion, and his mom's too. She poured her heart and soul into the kids in her fifth grade classroom. She helped both Bernie and his dad see that a great life was possible no matter where you started out. She had been the first person in her family to go to college, and the first to buy her own home.

The sisters hadn't stayed very close, but Ruby knew about some of Josh's troubles. Ruby and Catherine talked on the phone every few months, and even though she felt ashamed, sometimes Catherine told Ruby about Josh's latest stint in jail or failure at school.

Matt and Ruby had already talked a few times about the idea of Josh coming to live with them for a while. Ruby was worried about the stresses on her sister. Matt could imagine what life was like for his nephew, having seen many kids like him on his beat in Brooklyn. They hadn't told Bernie everything, but Bernie knew that Josh had dropped out of school. Anyway, Bernie was anxious to meet his cousin.

The summer that Josh was nineteen and Bernie was twenty, Ruby called Catherine with the offer for Josh to spend a month with them. They wouldn't do anything special; just welcome him into the family and their daily lives. And show him the life chests. Ruby had become the official life chest keeper of the family when their father had passed away five years earlier.

It was Catherine's last hope for Josh that spending time with his relatives in New York would help him straighten out his life and find some purpose. She only vaguely recalled the life chests but she knew her sister and family had something that she didn't have. Something that made life richer and gave it a deeper meaning. The day Catherine accepted Matt and Ruby's offer to take Josh in for a month started a series of changes that would add that richness and meaning to both their lives.

That was an unforgettable time in New York.

Josh was introduced to the power of the life chest and the lessons they contained.

It was the beginning of Josh's lifelong friendship with his cousin Bernie- and his years of jokes about Bernie's argyle sweaters!

During his month in New York, Josh took his first steps on the path to having a great life. After New York, Josh "got it". He understood what he needed to do to accomplish CANI (Constant and Never-ending Improvement) in his life. He was bursting with energy, ideas and promises. He wanted to make a great life for himself. He wanted to help his mom and his girlfriend Leah to have great lives, too.

But it took some doing. Old habits are hard to break. The lessons from the life chests were just the beginning for Josh, and he worked hard at putting them into practice. It took a while for his mom and for Leah to believe he really had changed. He got a job, cut ties with his former friends and began studying for his high school diploma before Leah was sure about taking him back, but she did. His mom was amazed to see him start helping out around the apartment, buying groceries, and even opening a savings account.

In some ways, though, it was rougher between Josh and his mom than they had expected it to be when he returned from New York. Catherine almost resented her son's new attitude. What about all he put me through? she thought. Is it all supposed to go away just like that? I've gone to hell and back because of that kid.

Moving on took some work. Josh was worried that he'd never be able to make it up to his mom. Maybe she'd never forgive him. For a while she wondered the same thing. She began talking to her sister more, and sharing her struggles and hopes. Ruby gave Catherine the encouragement she needed. "Forgiveness isn't easy," Ruby said in one conversation with her sister. "But it's important. You do it for yourself as well as for the other person. And your relationship can't move forward without it." Catherine took the advice to heart, and shared it with Leah, too.

Josh kept at it. Month by month, life was getting better; closer to the great life he wanted to have. But it wasn't exciting and dangerous anymore. Frankly, he missed the rush. Sometimes life felt ordinary and boring, and Josh got restless. When he felt the pull towards his old life or when a former friend pressured him to join in on a robbery or asked him to fence something, he'd call Bernie.

Bernie was farther along in his journey to making a great life than Josh was in his, but he didn't judge Josh; he encouraged his cousin. They talked about the things they were putting in their life chests. Josh had a picture of him and Leah that was taken on their first anniversary after getting back together. Bernie had his college graduation video.

They shared their goals, talking about what they wanted their futures to look like. Bernie was thinking about getting a master's degree. One thing Josh wanted was a job that made enough money so that he and Leah could be comfortable. He also wanted to keep the promise he had made to his mom—that he would buy her a house. It felt good to share their dreams and goals. It helped them to focus and it made their goals seem more attainable.

Matt, Ruby and Bernie made the trip to California for Josh and Leah's wedding in 2104. There were lots of happy tears, hugs and congratulations. Bernie, as best man, made a toast at the reception. "I am so proud of this guy," he said, holding up a glass of champagne. "He and Leah are making a great life, and they're an inspiration to me, too. Here's to their future!"

Josh and Leah started their new life together with hope, happiness and support from their families. There were rough spots here and there, but Josh kept the *Pumptitude* books within reach and the lessons he had learned from them close to his heart.

He kept in touch with Bernie, and they caught up on how their folks were doing, too. Bernie said that some of his parents' friends were thinking about retiring. Josh laughed at that one. "Uncle Matt and Aunt Ruby? They love what they do too much. They'll never retire."

Bernie had to agree. "How is your mom doing?" he asked. "I haven't talked to her much since your wedding last year."

"She's doing great," answered Josh. "She got a job as a teacher's assistant in a special needs classroom, and she really loves it. Her life chest is filling up with good stuff." He suddenly remembered another bit of news. "Guess what I just put in my life chest yesterday? The first ultrasound image. Leah and I are going to have a little girl, and you're going to be an uncle!"

"Congratulations!" exclaimed Bernie. "That's great!"

"Thanks. We're doing it right this time," said Josh.

It takes time and intention to fill your life chest. There are a lot of lessons along the way, some of them difficult to learn. But looking at the difference between his life now and his life just a few years earlier, Josh knew it was well worth the effort.

"I don't know if you want to talk about it, but I gotta ask," said Josh as he watched Bernie plop down on the sofa. "Is something going on? What's wrong?"

"I don't know what you mean," answered Bernie.

Josh shot him a look that said "you can't kid a kidder".

"Okay, you got me," Bernie admitted. "Have you noticed that I haven't talked much lately about Jessica? Well, she broke up with me. Hit me like a ton of bricks, to put it mildly."

"Wow. I'm so sorry."

"She doesn't want to get married. I guess I should have seen the signs. She was hinting at it for a while, but I didn't want to believe it. Not until she told me straight out that she was leaving me. I felt like a sap. And an idiot. Remember that dumb list I put in my life chest? All the qualities of my ideal woman? A lot of good that did me." Bernie sighed. "So I've been putting all my energy into graduate school, taking extra classes and tutoring. Between that and work, I guess I've been shutting everything else out. But I'll have my PhD in nanotech next year. You'll be able to call me Dr. Bernie."

Bernie tried to laugh but Josh could hear the sadness and even a hint of desperation in his cousin's voice. He didn't know what to do. He didn't want to say something stupid, so he laughed too and turned back to the life chest. "Doc," he said. "Let's find something cool in Great-Great-Grandpa Kim's life chest. Some old pictures of when they used to drive cars around on the ground or something. Come on."

Bernie plopped down on the floor next to Josh's chair. "You'd love one of those old cars, wouldn't you?" asked Bernie.

"You bet I would!" said Josh. He reached into the chest and picked up an old piece of leather, rolled and tied with a cord. "Hey, remember this?"

"What? That map?" asked Bernie.

"Yup. We looked at it the last day of my trip out here."

"Wow, ten years ago. You were such a scrawny kid."

Josh punched Bernie's arm. "You were a dweeb. And you still are. Seriously, is that the same argyle vest you were wearing the day you picked me up from the airport?" Josh kidded.

Bernie laughed. "Of course not. But I do buy them in bulk," he joked. "Saves money!"

Josh carefully untied the cord and spread the map out on the coffee table. The ancient leather was covered in drawings and Chinese characters.

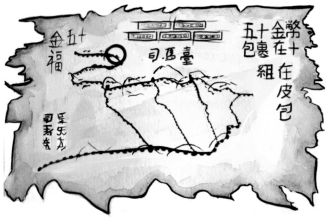

The ancient treasure map

"I remember this now. Something Gramps got the first time he went to Asia," said Bernie.

"Didn't he write about it in one of his journals?" asked Josh. "Let's find it."

After some digging in the life chest, they located the journal. Josh carefully paged through it till he found what he was looking for. "This is incredible, Bernie," said Josh as he looked at the journal. "Great-Great-Grandpa Kim sure wrote down a lot of great stories in his travel journals. This whole section is about his friend in Thailand. That's who gave him the map."

"It's a treasure map, remember?" said Bernie. "It shows where fifty ancient gold coins are buried in the Great Wall of China."

"Yeah, I remember that story. I wonder if they were ever found." Josh handed Bernie the journal and then picked up the map, studying the mysterious Chinese characters.

Bernie shook his head. "Doubtful. That's part of the whole thing." He pointed to a paragraph in the journal. "The legend is that the old man who hid the coins in the Great Wall made the map showing where they were, but he didn't tell anyone, not even his own family. Nobody knew about it for hundreds of years, I guess."

"Why did Gramps end up with the map? Does it say in the journal?" asked Josh. He got in a comfortable position on the floor next to his cousin, with the journal and map in front of them on the coffee table.

"Yes," said Bernie. "Remember reading this? Gramps met this man on a business trip to Thailand and they became friends. Gramps called him Mr. CC. He was from China, and he showed Gramps his family's chests. Those chests went back centuries! The first one was built by Marco Polo and given to his Sherpa guide. All sorts of awesome stuff got put in that chest, in hidden compartments and everything. That's how Gramps got the idea for the life chest business here in the U.S."

"I think Marco Polo was one of Gramps' heroes," chuckled Josh. "They were both travelers and storytellers. Anyway, the coins were hidden in the bottom of that chest—the Dynasty chest, right?"

"Yeah, for hundreds of years, till one of the descendants of Marco Polo's guide finally found them and decided to stash them in the Great Wall while it was being built," said Bernie. "This map is the only evidence that they ever existed, but I guess no one was ever sure if the story was true. Look, it says here in the journal that Mr. CC couldn't go back to China even if he wanted to, so he couldn't look for the coins. Gramps said he would if he ever got the chance, so Mr. CC gave him the map."

"I don't think he ever did go back," said Josh, scanning a few more pages of the old journal. "See? There's nothing in his journal about trying to find them."

"Hang on. There's something right here." Bernie pointed to a paragraph and read their great-great-grandfather's words. "I will try to keep my promise to Mr. CC, but the story of the coins and the map may be just a legend. Mr. CC wasn't sure if the coins ever really were in the Dynasty chest."

"I don't know," said Josh. "Why couldn't it be true? Stranger things have happened."

"I suppose," said Bernie. "Fifty ancient gold coins. Wow. They must be worth millions by now. But I guess we'll never know."

"You don't think so? We could find out. We've got the map, don't we?"

"Josh, this is China were talking about. On the other side of the world."

"So what? Let's go. Let's go there and find out! Take the map, go to the Great Wall, and find those coins! I bet Gramps felt bad that he never got to do it. Let's do it for him."

There was a glint in Josh's eyes. He was half kidding when he first thought of the idea, but the more he put it into words, the more he really wanted to do it. And this might be just what Bernie needed to get out of his slump. An adventure!

"You're crazier than I thought you were, Josh," said Bernie. "Go to China, and dig around the Great Wall, looking for a bunch of coins that might not even exist?"

"Bernie, listen." Josh stood up, getting more excited. "That map has been sitting in a life chest— first Mr. CC's, and then Gramps'—for hundreds of years. We both know there's something about a life chest that makes crazy things real; things you never would've imagined. You and I are living proof of that. We're here because of a story in a book that was kept in a life chest. Come on, man. We were meant to do this!"

Bernie smiled and shook his head. Josh was crazy for sure, but what the heck? There was nothing to lose, and maybe a lot to gain. Josh's enthusiasm could always get him going. It's like we play tag team, thought Bernie. When he's down I rev him up, and vice versa. "Okay, so what's the plan?" he asked. "Tell me all about it."

"I don't have a plan yet!" said Josh, pacing excitedly around the room. "I just now got the idea! But I'll plan it alright. I guess the first thing to do is to get this map translated."

"I'll take it over to the University," said Bernie. He stood, carefully rolling up the map. "I won't tell anyone what we're going to do, but I'll get some help figuring out what it says."

"Great. I'll look into getting out there and where we're going to stay and all that. And we should read those books about Marco Polo's travels again. You know, for inspiration."

"What's your wife gonna say to all this, Josh? And how are we gonna pay for it? I don't know," he said with uncertainty. "It seems like too much."

"Come on man, have big dreams and take big actions! Such is the effort; such is the reward, right? We're the Marco Polos of our generation!" replied Josh.

"You read *Pumptitude* too much, Josh." Bernie laughed.

"Impossible. Your logic is flawed." said Josh with a punch to Bernie's shoulder.

"You're gonna keep punching me until I agree to do this, aren't you?"

"You got it. So are we on?"

"We're on. So stop hitting me!" Bernie put some distance between himself and Josh's fist. "Our parents and Leah are going to think we're crazy, you know."

"We *are* crazy," responded Josh. "Always have been."

"Speak for yourself," said Bernie.

"Well, maybe you need a little more crazy in your life."

"Maybe I do." Bernie sighed. "Losing Jessica really threw me for a loop. And I need a break from writing my thesis. Okay, cousin. Let's go to China!"

— Chapter 15 —

China:

The Adventure Begins

Josh and Bernie spent the rest of the evening planning the trip. Their families weren't sure what to think at first, but the young men were so enthusiastic that they got everyone else on board. There were a lot of things to be done. They had to arrange to get off work and school. They had to borrow money. But they were determined to make this happen, especially Josh. He figured an adventure would get Bernie out of his funk, and he was worried about his cousin. Josh took his aunt and uncle aside and mentioned his concerns about Bernie. They thought the trip was risky, but agreed that it might be just the thing their son needed.

"You boys are something else," said Uncle Matt as the family sat around the breakfast table the next morning. "But I'm proud of you. You know what you want and you go for it."

"It would be exciting to find those coins after all these years," admitted Bernie. "What a discovery!"

"And can you imagine how much they'd be worth?" added Josh. "I'd be able to buy Mom and Leah and Meg everything they ever needed."

"We don't need a lot of money," insisted Leah. "We'll be fine with or without it. Besides, nobody even knows if those coins ever really existed, Josh. You might be going on a wild goose chase, honey."

"I know," said Josh, putting an arm around Leah's shoulder. "But wouldn't you love not having to worry about Meg's college tuition?" Turning to his mom, he said, "And I'm going to get that house I promised you, Mom. Believe it."

"I believe it," said Catherine with a smile. "Whether or not you find a stash of gold coins. Like Matt said, when you go after something, you get it."

"Hey, if nothing else, it'll be a great adventure. Right, Bernie?"

"Right. It sure will be," said Bernie. "And I need some adventure in my life right now. So, what do we do next?"

"Well, get that map translated. And we need to take money out of savings and pack and get visas and learn how to use chopsticks, I guess."

"We'll start today," laughed Aunt Ruby. "I'll make Chinese for lunch."

"I wonder if anyone besides us even remembers that map exists," said Josh. "That Mr. CC guy gave it to Gramps a long time ago, in 1983."

"So the map was Mr. CC's?" asked Leah. "Then if you find the coins, they really belong to his family, don't they?"

The room fell silent. "Yeah, I guess so. You're right," said Bernie. "Even if we find them, they're not ours to keep."

Josh burst out, "But we're doing all the work! We're taking all the risks! Spending the money to get there and everything! Come on! Finders keepers." He looked around for support. "Finders keepers, right?"

Nobody joined in to agree with him, and Josh felt ashamed. "Okay, okay. I shouldn't be making this about the money. You know what it is, really?" Josh straightened up and spread his arms expansively. "It's a life chest adventure! It doesn't matter if we get rich out of it. We're keeping Gramps' promise that he made to Mr. CC."

"That's the ticket, Josh," said Bernie. "We have to do this for Great-Great-Grandpa Kim. And don't forget," he laughed, "We're the Marco Polos of our generation!"

"Yup. And Marco Polo gave those coins away. So here's another thing to add to our to-do list. We'll find Mr. CC's family; let them know that we've got their map, and that we're going to look for the coins. If the coins exist, we'll find them, and give them back to the family."

"I'll go through the journals and find all the information I can about Mr. CC," said Aunt Ruby. "His descendants could still be in Thailand."

"I'll get the map translated," said Bernie.

"Your mom and I can help with the travel stuff," offered Leah. "Josh, you'll have to get approval for a leave of absence from work. If your boss approves it, you should probably stay here for the next couple of weeks, so you and Bernie can get the trip planned and leave for China together."

"I'll call my boss right away," agreed Josh. "Are you sure it would be okay to stay here, Aunt Ruby? And Leah, you'll have to go back home without me."

"No problem here," said Aunt Ruby. Everyone agreed that it was a good plan. "We'll be fine back in L.A.," Leah reassured Josh. "You're going to have some amazing things to put in your life chest when you get back!"

"I guess I'll go get some chopsticks to practice with," said Uncle Matt, laughing. He clapped Josh on the shoulder. "You've got a good attitude, Josh. You boys are doing the right thing. Good things will come back to you, don't worry. You'll have your success."

Catherine, Leah and Meg stayed on for a few extra days to help arrange flights, hotels and visas. On the morning they had to leave, Leah hugged Josh tightly before he climbed into the levicab that would take them to the airport.

the Great Wall. They pored over books on ancient and modern China, and they tried to glean every possible bit of information from the map. They scanned it, enlarged it, traced it, and uploaded all the images to Bernie's tablet.

Finally, almost three weeks after they decided to make the trip, Bernie and Josh were on the long flight to China. Josh held the map in a carry-on and refused to let it out of his sight. Bernie had the images and the translation saved on his tablet. He told Josh not to worry about the map. Logically, they didn't need it anymore, but Josh was insistent. He felt the power of the life chest and the artifacts that were stored in them more strongly than ever. He wanted that map with him for this entire quest. It was like a talisman.

Bernie pulled up the map on his tablet for the umpteenth time. He and Josh continued talking and planning how they were going to make this crazy thing happen.

"According to our research, the part of the Great Wall we need to go to was built on some pretty steep terrain," explained Bernie. "Tourists can only walk along the top of the wall. We're going to have to find some way to get down to the base, where the coins are hidden."

"Okay, so they're hidden inside the wall down at ground level?" asked Josh.

"That's what we got from the translation. It's in the Simatai section of the wall outside Beijing." Bernie pulled up another screen on his tablet. "Look, here's the birds-eye view of the wall where the map points to. And I can zoom down to ground level. I read that this is an area that gets very little tourist traffic."

"Good," said Josh. "The fewer tourists the better. We'll have to get there and check the place out first. See what kind of tools we need and everything. And we have to do it without drawing any attention to ourselves."

"Yup. You've always wanted to be a spy, right?" laughed Bernie.

"No, that was you. I was into superheroes." Josh laughed too, but then got serious. He had to ask Bernie a question that had been bothering him. "Bernie, we're heading into Beijing. We're actually doing this thing, and we might find those coins. I've got the address and comm number for Mr. CC's family in Thailand. When should we contact them?"

"I've been thinking about that, too," admitted Bernie. I think we should wait until we know something, good or bad. If we find the coins, it'll be a great surprise for them. And if we don't, then we haven't gotten their hopes up for no reason. We'll still call them, and let them know that we have the map and tried to find the coins."

"Sounds like a plan," said Josh. He yawned. "I'm gonna try to sleep. Wake me up if they start passing out food or something, okay?"

The long flight was eventually over, and Josh and Bernie were glad to be on the ground in Beijing. The weather was warm but cloudy. Bernie had done a crash course in Mandarin on the plane, and tried to explain their destination to a ground transport guide. His Brooklyn accent must have gotten in the way, because the man tried to get them to join a tour group of Australian Tai Chi teachers.

After a few confusing minutes, Josh remembered that Leah had printed an itinerary with the hotel name written in Chinese. He showed the guide the itinerary. "Ah! Chen Double Dragon Inn," said the guide. "Closest hotel to the Great Wall at Simatai, but small and run down. I can show you better hotels."

"No, thanks," said Josh. "This is the one we want."

They got on the bus to Simatai for the two-hour ride. Josh never understood how just sitting in a plane or a bus could make a person tired, but he was beat, and so was Bernie. They were both dozing off as the bus pulled up to their stop. It was a one-story, inexpensive family hotel, still several miles from the Great Wall, but the closest of all the area inns. Figuring they would rest before they looked around, the young men barely noticed their surroundings as they walked up to the front desk.

Bernie and Josh arrive at the Chen Double Dragon Inn

If they had been more attentive, they would have seen that the lobby was simply decorated in Chinese style, a bit shabby and old, but clean. They also would have seen that the young woman who checked them in (and thankfully spoke pretty good English) was strikingly beautiful, but had a restless, distracted air about her. Josh and Bernie, tired as they were, completely missed the intense gaze she fixed on them as they gathered their bags, and didn't see her quickly writing a few sentences in a small book after they thanked her and turned toward the stairs.

Once they were settled in their room and had checked in with the family back home, Bernie and Josh made a plan. Their goal was to hike the wall and the area around it, using the information from the map to pinpoint as closely as possible where the coins were hidden. They would figure out what was needed to extract the coins: whether they needed to dig, or use a pick to break away old rock or brick. They would probably have to damage the wall. Would they be able to get away with it? Would they be arrested? It was a worrisome thought, and after they talked about it, Bernie couldn't get it out of his mind.

Josh spoke up as he watched Bernie pace in their small room. "Bernie, let's cross that bridge when we come to it, okay? We'll have a better idea tomorrow of what we need to worry about when we see the wall."

"Okay, okay," sighed Bernie. "You're right. Let's get some sleep."

But Josh was wrong. Scoping out the wall in the morning wouldn't tell them everything they needed to know. What they really needed to worry about was right there in the hotel with them.

THE LIFE CHEST

— Chapter 16 —

Secrets at the
Chen Double Dragon Inn

Chen Mara, the owner of the Chen Double Dragon Inn, was a small, determined-looking woman, with steely eyes and gaunt features. She had been attractive when she was young, and her graceful figure had made her a good dancer. In adulthood, however, her grace had hardened into a practical, no-nonsense attitude that was unable to see any beauty or goodness in life.

"Daughter, where are you?" she called as she came into the kitchen that afternoon, carrying several shopping bags. "I need to see the registration book for today."

"I'm here, Mother," said Chen Li as she hurriedly entered from the back hall. "I took more clean towels to the German family."

Chen Li, a tall young woman with a sweet and honest face, was her only child. She had a beauty and goodness that Chen Mara looked past every day. There was no room for affection and happiness in their life together.

"More clean towels? You make sure you take all the soiled ones and count them. Why do they need so many towels?"

"Mother, they're large people. And our towels are small, you must admit." Chen Li laughed a little at the thought of the jolly German father wrapping himself in two or three towels after every bath.

"Just the same, make sure they're not stuffing the towels in their suitcases."

"Ha! If he believed that the Westerner would return the coins, he was a fool! If I found such riches, I would not give them away! It is fortunate that my ancestor Chen Mogwai created a chest to store his own treasures. Our family has five chests now. They hold jewels, jade pieces, and pearls. I am the keeper, and I am no fool. The chests are locked away in a closet next to my office. I show the treasures to no one, least of all Westerners who would try to trick me into giving them away!"

Chen Li tried a different tactic in one conversation. "I don't think your great-great-uncle really thought one of their ancestors hid fifty gold coins inside the Great Wall during the Ming Dynasty, did he? So the map was nothing more to him than an interesting drawing."

"A stupid conclusion," insisted Chen Mara. "Why give up even the chance for such treasure? Chen Cheng Gong was a weak and foolish man. We are Chen Mogwai's descendants. We are the strong branch of the family. And we will keep fighting for the wealth we are entitled to." With a sharp voice and a set jaw, Chen Mara always had the last word.

As she grew older, Chen Li mostly gave up arguing with her mother. Only once, when she was twenty-five, did she dare to say what she really thought. Out of overwhelming feelings of frustration and fatigue, she interrupted one of Chen Mara's daily tirades and said, "That map is probably a joke! A prank that's hundreds of years old. You fell for it and it's ruining our lives. Mother, you're really the fool!"

The sting of her mother's hand across her face had brought tears to her eyes and sorrow to her soul. From then on she behaved as a dutiful daughter. And here she was still, three years later, sitting at this front desk, trapped in a life with no way out.

The whistling teakettle brought Chen Li back to her duties. She prepared her mother's tea and carried it to the office. Chen Mara turned away from the window as her daughter handed her the warm, fragrant cup. She had been thinking about the past as well, and began to tell more of the story.

"My great-grandfather built this hotel so we could watch over the Great Wall. He had to bribe many officials and pull many strings in the government for them to allow us to build this close to the Wall. I helped my parents keep watch for anyone who might come here looking for the coins, and now you help me."

Chen Li had heard this part of the story many times, but she merely nodded and listened.

"You see, our family should be wealthy. We should be living in a mansion with many servants." Chen Mara gestured at her surroundings dismissively. "This is not what we deserve. This is the wrong we have to right." She spit out the next sentence with extra venom. "And it is the fault of my great-great-uncle and that Westerner, Kim Yost. Sooner or later, some relative of his will come here with that map. I live for the day I can trick them into finding the gold coins for me. For me!"

Chen Mara was energized by the thought of revenge and riches as she drained her tea cup. "Now go. Talk to the Americans. Get them to trust you. Find out their plans. Do your duty, Chen Li. They may be the ones we have been waiting for." She flipped a switch on a blinking device that sat on her desk. "The monitoring device is working. I will be listening."

Chen Li said nothing as she picked up the tea tray. Chen Mara watched her daughter and softened a bit, perhaps picturing herself at her age.

"Daughter, I was told the story from the time I was a young girl, just like you were. It was difficult for me too sometimes, but it's who we are. It's what we must do."

Chen Li simply said, "Yes, Mother," as she left the room. She didn't dare speak her thoughts, but they thundered in her head. Mother, why can't you see? I don't want this to be who I am. I don't live for the day of revenge, like you do. Her thoughts continued as she washed the tea things. I know I'm all you have since Father died. I want to be a good daughter, but your obsession means that I don't get to have a life. You won't let me go out with friends. You won't let me have any job other than here at the hotel, as your spy. I don't care about being rich or about getting revenge, but I can't tell you that. Chen Li put her hand to her cheek as a tear came to her eye. You would never understand, she thought sadly.

Looking around at the tidy kitchen, Chen Li shook herself out of her mood. Well, I can talk to myself all I want, but there is still a job to do, she said to herself. As she had heard Americans refer to it on TV, Chen Li put on her "game face". With a brisk walk and a tight smile, she grabbed a stack of clean towels from the linen room and headed up the stairs. The towels were for the Germans, but she would stop at the Americans' room first.

Josh and Bernie had showered and taken a short nap when Josh's comm beeped. "Time for some food!" Josh exclaimed, yawning. "You hungry?"

"Yeah, I guess I could eat. Let's get out and stretch our legs, anyway. We can unpack later." Bernie stood up from the bed to look for his shoes when they heard a light voice at the door.

"Hotel staff!"

"Come in," called Bernie, while Josh quickly glanced around to see if he had picked up his underwear.

Chen Li peeked in the doorway. "Excuse me. I want to welcome you again to our hotel. And to China. My name is Chen Li. This is your first visit? Are you here on business? "

Bernie shot Josh a quick look. Maybe they should play this close to the vest. "No, just a vacation. We've always wanted to see the—the Forbidden City."

"Yeah, we're doing that first thing, aren't we Bernie?" Josh understood the look and agreed. "We're going tomorrow morning."

"You will be amazed by the Forbidden City," said Chen Li. "I spent many hours there as a child. I loved wandering through the gardens alone. It's the most peaceful place I've ever been."

She picked up the brochure that Josh had set on the dresser, and started to hand it to Bernie. When their eyes met, Chen Li was surprised to feel so instantly comfortable with this redheaded American. She hadn't meant to keep talking about herself, but she couldn't help adding, "I forget all my troubles when I'm in the gardens of the Forbidden City. I can't hold sadness in my heart when I'm surrounded by such beauty."

Bernie took the brochure and their hands lightly touched. Chen Li suddenly felt embarrassed and dropped her gaze. "They provide tour guides, but I suggest you read through this literature before you go. It will make your experience much better."

"Thanks very much. I don't suppose you give tours yourself? It sounds like you know the Forbidden City very well. I sure would enjoy seeing it through your eyes," said Bernie.

Chen Li looked up, pleased in spite of her embarrassment. "Oh, no. I am not a guide. This is our family hotel, and I—I run the front desk."

"I bet you can tell us a good place to eat tonight," interjected Josh. "Bernie, I'm feeling pretty hollow."

"Anything I can help with, I will be happy to," said Chen Li.

Chen Mara was listening in, but it was a good thing that couldn't see her daughter's smile, because there was nothing false or calculated in her expression. It was completely genuine.

"Come to the front desk before you go out. I can suggest some fine restaurants," said Chen Li as she turned to leave.

"Wait! Your towels!" Bernie handed them to her.

"Oh, thank you. You can have these if you need extra."

"No, I think we have enough. Don't we, Josh?"

"Plenty," said Josh. "Thanks, Chen Li. We'll be down in a few minutes."

About a half hour later, Bernie and Josh ventured out to one of the restaurants Chen Li had recommended. As they walked, Josh stole a look at his cousin. "Whoa, Bernie! I'm surprised at you!" he chuckled. "Making a play for the locals already?"

"No, it was nothing like that," said Bernie. "I don't know, Josh. There's something about her. I can't explain it. I just feel like I could sit and talk with her for hours."

"Talk. Yeah, okay." Josh grinned.

Bernie didn't seem to hear his cousin's friendly dig as a new thought came to him. "Gosh, I hope she didn't think I was trying to pick her up. She's so pretty; I bet she gets guys annoying her all the time."

"Don't worry about it," said Josh. "I think she liked you, too."

"Oh, good!" Bernie quickly looked at Josh. "I mean—good that she wasn't insulted."

They had reached the restaurant, and Josh opened the door. "I knew that's what you meant. Now let's see how good your chopstick technique is."

— Chapter 17 —

Forbidden City, Dreaded Knowledge

While Bernie and Josh were enjoying their first dinner in China, Chen Li was in the middle of an argument in her mother's office. Chen Mara spoke with determination.

"I will work the front desk tomorrow, Daughter. I heard the Americans tell you that they are going to the Forbidden City in the morning. You will go with them."

"Must I, Mother? It will be awkward."

Chen Mara's voice rose in frustration. "They asked you to go with them! And you said no! How could you pass up that opportunity? You won't!"

"Mother, I can find out more information without—"

"Daughter, you will obey me! Go and leave a message for them. Tell them that you have a day off tomorrow, and you'll be happy to show them around the Forbidden City."

"Yes, of course, Mother. Forgive me."

"We must be diligent. We must keep close watch of every suspicious Westerner that comes here. Find out why they are in Beijing, and who their family is. Now go."

Chen Li hated deceiving people, but she loved the Forbidden City. It had been months since she had taken a day to walk through the gardens. It really would be lovely, and she

Josh's voice broke in. "You haven't! Let's move on, bro!"

Bernie turned red and Chen Li laughed. "We haven't reached my favorite part yet," she admitted. "The Imperial Garden."

"Let's go there now," said Bernie. "It sounds beautiful." Bernie was looking at Chen Li as he spoke, and was admiring her beauty as much as the colorful artwork in the Hall.

The green beauty of the plants and trees, the gentle sound of wind chimes, and the smell of incense in the Imperial Garden gave Chen Li a deep sense of peace, as always. They spent more than an hour walking among the juniper trees and scholars' stones, exploring the pavilions, and marveling at the giant rock structure called the Hill of Accumulated Elegance. Thoughts of her "mission" pushed their way forward but Chen Li shoved them to the back of her mind.

She just wanted to enjoy herself for once. She hardly ever got a chance to interact with people her own age, and Josh and Bernie were friendly and fun to be around. They were so different, though. Bernie stayed close to her side and seemed to drink in every word she had to say, while Josh kept running ahead or disappearing behind a pavilion or tree, only to pop out minutes later, shooting Bernie a big grin.

"I can see why this is your favorite place," said Bernie after Chen Li had explained how the garden was arranged. "But my feet need a break. Can we sit down for a minute?"

"Of course," said Chen Li hastily. They made their way to a bench under a blooming magnolia tree. After Chen Li sat down at one end, Bernie gave Josh a look while he scooted in next to her. Josh grinned and took the other end of the bench.

Chen Li leaned back and looked up into the magnolia tree branches. "This is what I used to do when I was a girl," she said. "Just stare up like this into the branches and the blossoms, and daydream the afternoon away."

The young people enjoy the beauty of The Forbidden City gardens

"Your family in Thailand—what's their name?"

"Chen. Both sides of the family are Chen," she replied.

Josh pulled Bernie to one side. "Excuse me, Chen Li, I'm sorry. Just a minute." He hissed to his cousin. "Bernie! What was that man's name in Thailand? The guy with the chests who gave the map to Gramps? This is crazy!"

"Relax, Josh," said Bernie. "Let's not be rude to Chen Li. Come on, let's just talk."

Bernie moved back to the bench. "Chen Li, one of our ancestors— our great-great-grandfather— had a friend in Thailand. Josh is freaking out over here thinking he could have been a member of your family."

"It's possible, isn't it?" asked Josh, still excited.

"You see," explained Bernie. "We know our family history, too. And it's for the same reason— the family chests. We call them life chests. Our great-great-grandfather started the life chest tradition in our family. He got the idea when he saw all the family chests that were held in keeping by his friend in Thailand. The legacy in those chests was incredible. He told our Gramps all sorts of stories about the history of his family."

"This can't be a coincidence!" said Josh excitedly, who was now pacing back and forth on the path.

Bernie sat on the bench next to Chen Li.

"Do you really think there's a connection?" Chen Li asked.

"Well, here's the kicker," answered Bernie. "Our Gramps was so impressed by his friend's stories that he wrote them down in his own journals. We learned all this when we found the journals in his life chest. The story you just told us about your ancestor, the elephant keeper's daughter? We read that same story. "

"You haven't told her the real kicker!" said Josh, sitting down on the other side of Chen Li. "The oldest chest in his family collection belonged to Marco Polo's guide. We're talking about the same guy here!"

All Chen Li could think as she looked back and forth between Josh and Bernie was that she was glad she was sitting down. She was honestly afraid she might have fainted if she were standing up. This was truly unbelievable. She tried to find her voice.

"You're right, Josh." Chen Li tried to sound calm. "It does sound like there is a connection between our families. Do you remember what his name was? Your ancestor's friend in Thailand?"

"His name?" wondered Josh. "Bernie, do you remember?"

"I don't know his Chinese name. Our great-great-grandfather called him Mr. CC in his journals."

Chen Li thought for a moment. "That may have been a name he used with Americans. It would be C for Chen, of course."

"So if his first name started with C, then we've got our man!" said Bernie.

"It's got to be the same guy," said Josh.

"I can find out his first name. It certainly may be the same person," agreed Chen Li. "What good fortune that you happened to come to our hotel!"

Bernie and Josh laughed. Chen Li laughed too, but her laugh was far from carefree. It was to cover up her feelings of dread and panic while she stalled for time. She knew the answer. They were talking about her mother's great-great-uncle, Chen Cheng Gong, the family chest keeper who gave away that map to a Westerner one hundred years ago.

"It sure was lucky," said Bernie. "Let's talk some more about our families. Maybe at dinner tonight. Does your mother have a life chest? Your father?"

The mention of her mother hit Chen Li hard. She stood up. No more stalling, no more talk. It was time to leave the beautiful garden and face reality. It wasn't good fortune that Bernie and Josh were staying at their hotel. It was bad fortune, and it was time to find out how bad it really was. "And your ancestor's name? Your Gramps?" she asked casually.

"Kim Yost," said Josh.

This time, Chen Li wasn't afraid of fainting. She had been prepared for the answer, and her response to Bernie's question was abrupt. "Thank you for the invitation, Bernie. I'm afraid I can't have dinner tonight. I apologize. I have to go back to work this evening." Chen Li picked up her purse and began to walk toward the north gate exit. "I'm glad you enjoyed the Forbidden City. We should start back so we don't miss the transport."

"Okay," said Bernie, picking up his step to catch up with Chen Li. "I hope you don't have to work every night this week. I'd like to have dinner sometime."

Chen Li stopped and turned. This was the hardest part of all. These Americans were her mother's enemies, it was certain now, and Chen Li was expected to bring back information on them. They could not be her friends, especially not sweet, sincere Bernie, with his ready smile and eyes that lit up when he looked at her.

She put on her game face again. The next thing she had to find out was whether they had the map, and she might as well use a dinner date to get the information. "I'd like that, too. I'll ask my mother. I'm sure she'll let me have some time off tomorrow night."

— Chapter 18 —

Alliances and Betrayal:

The Quest for the Treasure

Usually, Chen Li hated riding the busy transports at the end of the day, but now she was grateful for the crowds and the noise. She managed to get separated from Josh and Bernie and ended up sitting across the aisle from them. She just couldn't talk right now. She took a deep breath and tried to relax. Her mother would want a report as soon as they got back. Even if Chen Li didn't tell her everything, Chen Mara had the Americans' room bugged. As much as she tried to imagine a way that she could hide this information from her mother, she knew it was impossible. She had to think of some way to keep what she had discovered to herself as long as she could.

When they got off the transport car for the short walk back to the hotel, Chen Li hurried ahead, using the excuse that she had to get back to make her mother's tea. Bernie and Josh decided to stop off at a restaurant.

Once inside the family quarters of the hotel, Chen Li tried to sneak quietly to her room, but Chen Mara had been waiting for her. Before Chen Li could open her bedroom door, her mother grabbed her arm and led her into the kitchen.

"Daughter! Tell me everything! What did you find out about the Americans?"

"Mother, please let me sit down. I'm very tired."

"Yes, of course. I'll make the tea." Chen Mara put the kettle on and pulled up a chair next to Chen Li. "All right, what do you suspect? What are their plans?"

Chen Mara insists that her daughter spy on the Americans

Chen Li tried to stall. She wasn't going to tell her mother anything she didn't have to. "It was hard to get information out of them. They asked so many questions about the Forbidden City. Really, that's all we talked about. I will have to sit down with them in a place that has fewer distractions, so I can ask questions and not arouse their suspicion."

"How should you do it?" asked Chen Mara. "Go to their room? Do they need towels?"

"No," said Chen Li quickly. If she talked to Bernie and Josh in their room, her mother would no doubt be listening in. "One of them asked me to go to dinner with him. I said I was busy working tonight, but I would ask you if I could go tomorrow night. I'll be able to get all the information we need from him then."

"Not until tomorrow night? Well, all right. And until then, I'll have the listening device on. Thank you, Daughter. Go back to the front desk. Here, take your tea. After I drink mine I'll go to the office to listen in on them. If they are Kim Yost's relatives, and are here to steal the coins, they may start talking about it."

"Yes, Mother."

"I won't let them get away with it, Chen Li! Nothing is more important than getting what belongs to me!"

"Mother, please relax and drink your tea. I need to check the messages at the front desk. The Germans may need more towels."

"Those Germans!" Chen Mara shook her head as she sighed and added sugar to her tea.

For the moment, Chen Li had been successful in hiding what she had learned, but she had to move fast. Josh and Bernie would certainly talk over today's events once they got back to the hotel. She knew now that they were the people her mother had been waiting for all these years: Kim Yost's relatives. It was likely that they had the map with them and planned to search for the coins. There was no telling what her mother might do once she found out. Chen Li had to find a way to stall some more.

She hurried to the linen closet and grabbed a stack of clean towels. The Germans hadn't said they wanted any more, but she needed a reason to go up to the guest rooms. She had to talk to Bernie and Josh before her mother could get back to the office and turn on the listening device.

Chen Li glanced into the lobby. Bernie and Josh had returned and were heading to their room! She raced up the stairs and knocked on their door, barely waiting for an answer before rushing in.

"Hello," she said breathlessly. "Bernie, my mother has given me permission to have the night off tomorrow. I would be delighted to have dinner with you."

Bernie smiled broadly. "That's great! Josh, um, you're welcome to come along if you want. I'm sure—"

"No, no, no," protested his cousin with a wave of his hand. "I'm looking forward to relaxing right here and seeing what's popular on Chinese TV. You two kids go ahead and have fun," he said with a smile.

"Oh!" Chen Li had the idea she needed. "That's the other thing I meant to tell you," she said as she picked up the remote control and turned on the large screen TV that was mounted into the wall. She searched for the channel she wanted while she spoke. "There's a special on Beijing opera. They've been live streaming performances all day and the main production is just about to start. You must watch it. Beijing opera is my favorite of all the regional operas."

Chen Li aimed a thousand-watt smile at Bernie. "We can talk about it at dinner tomorrow night. I'd love to hear what you think of it. In fact," Chen Li scrambled for another hook. "One of my school friends is a featured dancer in the finale. He dances with three swords." One more thousand-watt smile, directed at Josh. "You will love it, Josh. Make sure to watch till the end!" Chen Li turned up the volume as high as she dared. "Well, I must deliver these towels. Enjoy the opera!"

She smiled again as she slipped into the hall, quickly closing the door behind her. She made her way to the front desk as fast as she could. If the Germans came down for extra towels, she'd have them right there. And if Bernie and Josh came down to report their missing remote control, she wouldn't have any idea where it was. She released a long sigh as she slipped the remote from under the pile of towels and into a drawer. This had to work. At least long enough for her mother to get frustrated and retire for the night.

An hour later, Chen Li could still hear the crashing cymbals and loud horns of the opera coming from Josh and Bernie's room. The poor boys, she thought. She hoped there really was a sword dance in the finale.

Chen Mara came around the corner from her office. "Of all things! They are watching Beijing opera! And the volume is so loud! If they are talking I cannot hear a thing. This has given me a headache. Please prepare some medication for me and bring it to my bedroom."

Chen Li jumped up. "Of course, Mother. Right away." After her mother was settled in bed, Chen Li peeked up the stairs. She pointed the remote control at Josh and Bernie's room and touched the 'off' button. No reason to torture them any longer. She'd sneak the remote back into their room tomorrow while they were out.

Bernie and Josh were up early the next morning, ready to explore the Great Wall of China. Since the Chen Double Dragon Inn was the closest hotel to the Simatai section of the wall, they ran a special shuttle bus to take guests there. Bernie and Josh were among a dozen people on the bus that morning. The shuttle operator told the group that they could see a large section of the wall from where the bus stopped, but could also hike on to a steeper section. He explained that parts of the wall at Simatai had been largely untouched since the 1600s.

Josh kept the map safely in his backpack, but Bernie had his tablet out and checked and rechecked coordinates. Neither of them said much, but they were excited about pinpointing the location where the coins had been hidden. Yup, Josh thought to himself with a smile. The Marco Polos of our generation!

The day was cool, but unusually sunny. Most of the group toured the part of the wall nearest the bus stop and then visited a café for lunch. Bernie and Josh were the only ones who hiked on to the hillier section. They munched on trail mix as they walked. The path along the top of the wall became more and more hazardous, with broken brick and loose stones slowing their pace.

"If this is all we eat today, I'm going to be really hungry for dinner tonight," remarked Bernie. "Are you sure you don't want to come with me and Chen Li?"

"Naw, I don't want to cramp your style," teased Josh. "I'll be perfectly content ordering in and watching more sword dancing on TV. I hope I can find the remote. Weird how the TV turned itself off last night. Were we supposed to deposit money in it or something?"

"I don't think so. I'm just glad it went off."

"Well I hope we didn't break it or anything," finished Josh. "Hey, what have you got on your tablet? I want to compare it to the map." He pulled the map out of his backpack and they leaned to rest on a still-intact section of the wall.

"I scanned the map, and after I got it translated, I put all the information in this document," said Bernie, pointing to his tablet. "There's a detailed drawing of the section we're looking for. I don't know how helpful it's going to be, since the wall must have deteriorated a great deal since 1640. But the person who drew it was pretty precise. Some of the bricks were stamped with the number of the army regiment that built this section. See the drawing of a brick on the map right there? The coins are buried near that brick. The instructions on the map said to start there, and count seven bricks up and seven bricks to the right. That's where the coins would be found."

Josh peered closely at the tablet. "I hope the numbers on the bricks are still readable," he said.

"Me too," agreed Bernie. "Anyway, I was able to estimate the location with my GPS. Then we can find the right spot and start digging." He looked up from the tablet and back at the ancient map. "I wonder if the man who drew this meant to go back and get the coins himself, or if he made the map for someone to find in the future."

"I wonder if somebody copied it like we did and found the coins years ago. Maybe even centuries ago," said Josh.

"Well, we're here now to take our crack at it. And whether it's millions of dollars in coins or an empty hole, I'm determined to find out something." Bernie jumped up. "The GPS is pointing a couple hundred yards from here down the wall. Let's go."

The further they walked, the rougher the path became. The most popular part of the wall, and the easiest for tourists to walk, was right outside Beijing. That section of the wall had been repaired and rebuilt so much that the Chinese now called it the New Wall. If the coins had been hidden there, it would have been impossible to search for them—there would be far too many people around, and the wall had been reinforced many times. Out here it was crumbling in many areas.

"Okay," said Bernie as they arrived. "Here we are. I guess we're lucky this spot is so deteriorated. It'll make it easier to dig into the side of the wall without leaving evidence."

Josh looked down over the crumbling wall. "You think it's lucky? We have to dig at the base of the wall where it meets the ground, right?" he asked. "How do we get down there from up here on top?"

"Good question," said Bernie as he peered over the edge. They were about ten feet above where they needed to dig. "Let's walk back."

"What? Are we giving up?"

"Of course not. But I saw a section of the wall about a quarter mile back that's broken down almost to the base. We can climb over that without any trouble, and then make our way back here."

"Sounds like a plan, boss," agreed Josh.

In a short time, Josh and Bernie found themselves back at the part of the wall they planned to dig into, this time at ground level.

"This is it!" exclaimed Bernie excitedly as he double checked the coordinates on his tablet and ran his hand over the bricks. "The numbers are worn, but I'm sure this is the right brick." He turned back to Josh. "What tools do you think we'll need here?"

"A shovel, and probably a pickaxe," said Josh, studying the wall. "It looks like it'll be pretty easy to get into this section. You're right. We *are* lucky. If this is the right place, it won't take long. Oh, we'll need another backpack for the coins, too. A sturdy one. They'll be heavy."

"You're doing quite well," Chen Li smiled. She hadn't minded at all what Bernie said. It was lovely, in fact. Just for an hour or two more, she wanted to shut out the world and enjoy this time without thinking about gold coins, bitter history, and her mother's desire for revenge. She didn't want to ask the prying questions. She didn't want to find out if they had the map and what they planned to do with the coins. Just for an hour more, she wanted to be happy.

But she didn't have an hour. A minute later, without meaning to, Bernie brought her back to the harsh reality of the situation.

"We had a really good hike out at the Great Wall today," he said. "The Simatai area is fascinating." Bernie couldn't help it. He was bursting with the news. He wanted to tell Chen Li about the good fortune that might be coming her way. He wanted to share this adventure with her. "Chen Li, we said we were going to wait to tell you, but I can't. We're not just tourists. We're exploring the Great Wall for a special reason."

"Oh? What is it?" Chen Li tried to keep her facial expression, and her emotions, as neutral as possible. She would hear what he had to say, and then? Don't think about it, she told herself. Just listen.

Looking into Chen Li's beautiful eyes, Bernie spilled everything. He told Chen Li about the map, about Mr. CC giving it to Great-Great-Grandpa Kim, about Gramps not going back to look for the coins, and about Josh talking him into coming to China to keep the promise and find the treasure. After a few minutes, he noticed an odd look on Chen Li's face. He figured she must be wondering if he and Josh were going to try to claim the coins as their own. He was quick to reassure her.

"Chen Li, this is about your family's legacy. Our great-great-grandfather told your mother's great-great-uncle that he would try to find the coins for him if he could. Josh and I want to do that. We know where Mr. CC's descendants are in Bangkok. If we find the coins, we plan on going straight to Thailand with them. But now we know you're part of the family too. I'm sure your relatives in Bangkok will be willing to share the coins with you, right? And your mother will be so happy! Should we go back now and tell her all about it?"

"No," said Chen Li quietly. "No, Bernie. It can't be that way. I wish with all my heart that it could be. But it can't."

She sat without speaking for a few moments, not knowing how to continue. Bernie stared at her, trying to figure out what was wrong. Finally, Chen Li looked up at him.

"Bernie, you are an honorable man. I can see that your family values truth and integrity. Your heart is full of trust." She wanted to add something, but couldn't look in his eyes while she said it. "And love."

Then Chen Li laughed—a harsh, bitter laugh, which confused Bernie. This tone of voice from the beautiful girl he was growing close to was something new to him.

"Those wonderful qualities won't do you any good here," she said. "In fact, they're putting you in danger."

"In danger? Chen Li, what do you mean? I don't understand."

"My mother will be happy to hear that you have the map. But not for the reason you think."

Bernie started to speak.

"Please, don't interrupt. I must tell you the whole story at once or I won't be able to say it at all." Chen Li took a deep breath and began again. "My mother learned the story of her great-great-uncle and Kim Yost when she was a little girl. This is the way her grandfather told it to her." Chen Li forced herself to look at Bernie. He had to know she was being honest with him.

"My mother's great-great-uncle, the man you call Mr. CC, was a weak and foolish man. Kim Yost was a greedy Westerner. He tricked Mr. CC into giving up the map, and he went back to

Chen Li continued her story. Now that she had someone to talk to, all her thoughts came rushing out. "I don't want the same things out of life that my mother does. She says that I don't have the same drive that Chen Mogwai passed down to his descendants. And I don't. I'm more like the other side of the family. My mother calls them weak and foolish but I think they're kind and unselfish. I look at my mother's life and see how unhappy she's been all these years, and I'm sad for her. I suppose she couldn't help turning out the way she did. She was taught by her father and grandfather. And when my father died it got even worse. After he was gone, she had nothing else to live for but finding the map and the coins. She's miserable. And she blames her great-great-uncle for everything."

"That's one of the reasons she's miserable," offered Bernie. "You can't be happy unless you take responsibility for your own life, the good and the bad. You have to own the choices you make and deal with the consequences."

"Yes. You are wise for such a young man."

"I don't mean to preach. I must sound pretty self-righteous," said Bernie, a bit embarrassed.

"No. What you say is true." Chen Li fell silent. Maybe that is what I need to do, she thought. I've been going along with my mother even though I know it's wrong. It may be time to take responsibility for my own life.

As if to begin, she stood up. "Let's go back to the hotel," she said. "We need to tell Josh about this."

As Chen Li waited for Bernie to pay the bill, she thought more about what it would mean to take responsibility for her own life. Should she tell her mother the truth about Josh and Bernie, or keep the news of the map a secret? Chen Li wasn't sure yet what she was going to do, but she resolved from this moment on to start living her life differently: to start having a life of her own.

Back at the hotel, she waited on the patio while Bernie went up to get Josh. When they came down, Chen Li explained why they needed to talk outside. "Let's walk down to the road," she said. "You see, my mother has a listening device in your room. Anyone who she considers suspicious is put in that room so she can listen in on their conversations."

"You mean our room is bugged? That's some serious spying," said Josh as they walked.

"I knew Mother was listening when we came back from the Forbidden City. That's why I made you watch the Beijing opera. She couldn't hear anything over that noise."

"I couldn't hear myself think over that noise!" said Josh.

"I kind of liked it," said Bernie.

"I did like the swordplay," admitted Josh.

Chen Li and Bernie filled Josh in on everything they had talked about at dinner. Josh listened without much comment. He could tell that Chen Li was upset, and torn between her loyalty to her mother and her affection for them, her new friends. Especially Bernie. But maybe it really wasn't as bad as all that. Josh spoke up.

"Can't we get your mother to understand? We're looking for the coins on behalf of your family. We're not planning on keeping them. Maybe if we just tell her that—"

"I'm sorry, Josh," Chen Li interrupted. "My mother would never trust you. You're Westerners and the descendants of Kim Yost. She would never consider you as anything but her enemies. She hates our family in Thailand, too. She doesn't want the coins to go to them. She won't settle for anything less than possession of all fifty coins."

They began to walk back to the hotel, silent for a few minutes, until Bernie spoke. "So now what, Chen Li? Can't we help at all?"

"Whatever I do will be my decision. You've inspired me to take responsibility for my own life now, Bernie. I don't know exactly what I'm going to say to Mother, but I will not let her threaten you."

"Thanks, Chen Li. That means a lot," said Bernie. "But your relationship with your mother is important. I don't want you to do anything on our behalf that might hurt it." He reached for Chen Li's hand, but she took a step away.

"I'm doing this for myself," said Chen Li staunchly. "Not because I like you." Her face flushed. "Not that I don't like you. I do. Both of you," she added as she quickened her step, embarrassed.

"We like you too," said Josh. "Both of us," he added, as he grinned at Bernie and dodged a shoulder punch from his cousin, making Chen Li laugh in spite of herself. Then Josh thought of something else. "Does your mother know we're out here, Chen Li? Is she going to be suspicious of us talking like this?"

"It's late. I know she's waiting to talk to me, but I'm sure she's in her bedroom. Don't worry." By now they were back on the patio.

"Still, we better not stay out here too long," said Josh. "I guess we'll stick to our plans for tomorrow, Bernie?"

"Yes." Bernie turned to Chen Li. "From the map and my analysis of it, I think we've got it nailed down pretty closely where the coins are hidden in the wall at Simatai." Bernie's voice rose a little in his eagerness to explain the details of the plan. "We've got a taxi coming for us early tomorrow, before daybreak. We'll drive to Simatai and dig for the coins before any security guards come on duty. The whole thing might be over and done with before you and your mother even wake up in the morning. We'll talk when we get back. If there's nothing in the wall, then there's nothing for your mother to fight over. If we have the coins, I guess we shouldn't tell her. We'll get to Bangkok as soon as possible and let Mr. CC's family decide what to do. Will you be working the front desk in the morning, Chen Li?"

"Yes. I'll try to behave as if it's a normal day. But I'll be worried about you."

Bernie and Chen Li looked into each other's eyes but were interrupted by Josh. "Both of us?" he teased.

Chen Li laughed. "Yes, both of you." She punched Josh on the shoulder.

"Ow! What have you been teaching her, Bernie?"

"Shh. We should probably go in now," said Bernie.

"Okay," said Josh as he opened the door. "See you inside."

Chen Li and Bernie turned to each other. "You go in first," said Chen Li. "I'll follow in a few minutes. And don't forget, my mother has the listening device in your room," she reminded Bernie.

"Right," he answered. "We'll just talk about football."

Bernie didn't want to go the room. He didn't want to leave Chen Li. He wanted to stand and stare into her eyes all night. No, what he really wanted was to take her in his arms and kiss her. But it wasn't the right time for that yet. He was worried about her and what she would say to her mother. He was worried about searching for the coins. Instead of speaking any of his thoughts, though, he smiled, kissed her on the forehead and went inside.

Chen Li stood at the door for a moment, taking it in. Bernie had kissed her. Just a sweet kiss, on the forehead, but her heart raced. Not now! she thought. She had to keep her wits about her. Her mother would be waiting for the information she had promised to get. She had to put Bernie out of her mind and put on her game face again.

Chen Li entered the hotel and walked as quietly as she could down the hall to the family quarters, heading for her room. She dared to hope that Chen Mara had fallen asleep, but she didn't get past her mother's bedroom door.

"Daughter! Is that you? Come in at once."

Chen Li obeyed, but she wasn't nervous any longer. She had decided what to do. She began her act as soon as she walked through the door and dropped into a chair.

"Oh, Mother. I despise watching Americans try to use chopsticks. You should have seen them. I don't know why they bother."

"Never mind about that. Tell me what you found out. Are they related to that thief, Kim Yost? Do they know about the coins?"

"They're no threat to us. They run a virtual hiking business. Have you seen those? They film themselves hiking in places around the world and sell the footage to virtual reality companies. The dull one who took me to dinner told me they have the idea that they're going to film all of the Great Wall of China as they hike. You should have seen his face when I told him it would take a year to walk the entire wall. They're as foolish as can be." Chen Li stretched and yawned. "I'm glad that's finished, anyway. Do you mind if I go to bed now, Mother?"

Chen Mara didn't answer. Chen Li glanced at her. The look on her face was strange. Was something wrong? Chen Li tried to keep a casual tone to her voice. "Did you have your tea tonight, Mother?" she asked.

"Yes, thank you, Daughter," Chen Mara answered. "You may go to bed."

"Are you all right? You—you don't still suspect the Americans, do you?"

"No. It is as you say. Every time Americans or Canadians arrive here, I both fear and hope that they have the map. It is a disappointment."

"I understand. Good night, Mother."

Chen Li felt relieved, but a little sick to her stomach as she walked down the hall to her bedroom. She hated lying. Well, tomorrow would tell. Whether or not Josh and Bernie found the coins, this was all going to end soon, she told herself. Even so, she couldn't completely relax. She certainly didn't think she'd be able to sleep well.

Chen Mara had been restless all evening, too. Waiting for Chen Li to come back from her dinner date, she passed the time updating supply records in her office. The window was open and she heard laughter as the three young people approached the hotel. She quickly turned off the lights and stood by the window, watching and listening. She heard everything Bernie said on the patio and silently congratulated her daughter on discovering the Americans' plans. But then she saw Bernie kiss Chen Li.

Chen Mara senses betrayal

What was this? Chen Mara's thoughts raced. She grasped for some kind of meaning in what she had seen. Why would her daughter let this American stranger kiss her? What could she be thinking? And then it hit. Chen Mara's twisted mind imagined her own daughter betraying her to gain the coins for herself. She became so angry that she wanted to scream. But she composed herself, left the office, went into her bedroom, and waited for Chen Li to walk down the hall.

Their conversation became a loyalty test, and Chen Li failed it. After her daughter left the room, Chen Mara's anger overcame her. Betrayal! Her only child! She seized a photograph of Chen Li and tore it to pieces. That would do for now. She wouldn't confront Chen Li tonight. The foolish girl would run straight to the Americans! No, her daughter would feel Chen Mara's anger in the morning. She had enough information to be able to follow the Americans out to the wall and ambush them there. And Chen Li would help her, whether she liked it or not. Chen Mara picked up the torn photo and threw the pieces into the trash.

Bernie and Josh slept lightly, too. Neither of them needed the alarm to get them up and dressed. They were in the lobby ready to meet their taxi twenty minutes before it was due to arrive. Chen Mara was awake, hiding in the kitchen. She listened to Josh and Bernie talk in the lobby. Every fiber of her being wanted to rush out and confront them, but she held back. She knew they had the map. She knew they were driving to Simatai and hiking to where the coins were hidden in the wall. Let them do the hard work, she decided. She would show up in plenty of time to claim her coins. As soon as Bernie and Josh drove off, Chen Mara sprang into action.

Chen Li was dreaming fretfully when she heard the pounding on her door. "Daughter! Daughter! Get out of bed immediately!" Chen Mara called.

"Mother, what is it? Wait, I'll be right there." Chen Li opened the door. Her mother burst into the room.

"Come with me. Your friends, the Americans, are on their way to find the coins. I know they have the map. I know you've been lying to me. Did they tell you they would share the coins with you if you helped them? Then they are liars too."

Chen Mara walked quickly down the hall to the lobby. Chen Li followed, protesting. "Mother, no! I was only—"

"We will follow them in the hotel shuttle bus." Chen Mara said as she took the vehicle's keys off the hook. "You will drive."

Chen Li tried again. "Mother, there's no need for this."

"No need?" Chen Mara spat back. "We can finally get back from these Westerners what they've stolen from us. From my great-great-grandfather Chen Mogwai on down—we are all victims of Kim Yost's thievery. I'll have revenge on his descendants!"

"But Bernie and Josh aren't trying to steal the coins! They want to—"

"Save your words, Daughter. You have betrayed my trust. Nothing you can say will change my mind about them."

As Chen Mara opened her purse to put the keys in it, Chen Li saw a handgun. She gasped.

Chen Mara fixed a cold stare on her daughter. "I'll do whatever I must to get back what belongs to me. Now go! Hurry and dress."

Chen Li rushed to her room, her mind and heart racing. She thought about her options as she quickly dressed. Her mother had a gun. What should she do? Chen Mara wanted her to drive the shuttle bus. She could refuse. But her mother was desperate. Bernie and Josh's lives were in danger. Chen Li had to go with her mother, to stop her from doing something terrible.

Chen Mara pounded on the door. "Daughter! We must go! Come!"

"I'm ready, Mother."

Mother and daughter walked in silence to the shuttle bus. Chen Li started the motor and pushed the route button for Simatai. The bus glided out of the driveway.

"Daughter, drive faster," Chen Mara barked.

Chen Li ignored her mother's command. "Mother, please listen to me." Maybe she could get her mother to calm down. She would have to listen while they were in the bus together. "I've been trying to tell you that Bernie and Josh are good people. They're not trying to steal from you."

"Ha!" Chen Mara's contempt was obvious. "Daughter, you believe them over your own mother? I am very disappointed in you. I raised you to be loyal to your family. Not to throw away our ideals because an American charms you."

"Loyalty? Our family ideals?" Chen Li finally found her voice and spoke her truth. "Mother, our ideals are nothing to be proud of, and nothing I've ever wanted to be loyal to."

Chen Mara tried to interrupt. "These Americans have brainwashed you. They have flattered you and appealed to your vanity. I didn't think you were such a fool."

"Mother, you are going to listen to me now." There was a passion to Chen Li's voice that surprised Chen Mara. The young woman punched the autopilot button and turned to her mother.

"This has nothing to do with the Americans. You have tried to teach me selfishness, bitterness and greed. You have shown me how to blame others for my misfortunes instead of taking responsibility for my own life. That's wrong, Mother. It has not given you a good life. It's made you miserable and I want no part of it. I don't want revenge. I don't care if the coins exist or not. I want to be a loving daughter, but I cannot live the way you want me to."

"You want to be my loving daughter? Then obey me!" said Chen Mara.

"Even though I do not honor and respect the things you stand for? I'm sorry, Mother, but I need to take responsibility for my own life." Chen Li began to gather strength from finally speaking her mind. Her voice became stronger as she continued.

"If the only way I can be a good daughter is to support you in your selfishness and desire for revenge, then we have both failed. I'm not an obedient daughter because you are not a loving mother. Your life is filled with hate, and such a life does not deserve obedience and respect." Chen Li glanced at the road, then back at the passenger seat. Chen Mara was staring straight ahead.

"Please," Chen Li continued, hoping to break through to some feeling in her mother. "Don't you see? Isn't it better to live with forgiveness, love and understanding? I do not want to live a life with no love in it. I want to trust people. I want to see the good in people. You only see evil, even when there isn't any. Can't you see the good? In the Americans? In me?"

"My life will be good when I get what I deserve," said Chen Mara through clenched teeth. "When I get the riches that belong to me. That is what I live for. No more talk, Daughter. Drive. We will be there soon."

Chen Li was near tears as she took the bus off autopilot and stepped harder on the gas pedal. She had poured out her heart to her mother and gotten nothing in return. They drove the remainder of the journey in silence.

THE LIFE CHEST

— Chapter 19 —

Confrontation at the Great Wall:

Reward and Destiny

Josh gave a generous tip to the taxi driver when they got to Simatai, and sent him on his way. It was still dark, but having done the hike the day before, he and Bernie were able to make their way with a flashlight without much trouble. They talked while they walked.

"You've got everything we need in the backpack, right?" asked Bernie.

"Yeah, of course," answered Josh. "That collapsible pick and shovel we got yesterday and a bag for the coins. I've got the map, too."

"Well, I've got all the information on my tablet," assured Bernie. "You really didn't need to bring the map."

"I wouldn't have come here without it. Even if we don't need it, it's like my good luck charm. Just think, Bernie, we're taking the map back to the place where that old man created it. We gotta have it with us when we do this."

"Okay, okay. I just trust the technology more to actually get us where we need to go."

"Fine. What does the technology say now? Are we close?" asked Josh.

"We're getting there," said Bernie. "I hope nobody sees us busting into the wall. Sure wouldn't want to end up in a jail cell in China."

"Yeah. Take it from me, cousin. Jail cells are no fun," Josh said wryly. "But hopefully we won't damage the wall too much. That section is already falling apart. And finding those coins would sure benefit a lot of people."

"I hope Chen Li's mother will be able to deal with it. I'm worried about Chen Li. I know she's concerned about what her mother might do if she knew we had the map."

"If we find the coins, maybe we can give a couple of them to her right away. And then take the rest to Thailand. I bet she'd be okay with that."

"I guess we shouldn't worry about it until we actually have something to worry about; till we actually have the coins in our hands." Bernie looked at his tablet. "Okay, Marco Polo. This is the spot."

"This is it?" asked Josh excitedly. "Right here?" He shined his flashlight on the wall at the spot Bernie had pointed to.

Bernie looked closely at the tablet. "This is where we were yesterday. According to the translation, we start from this brick, count seven bricks up, seven bricks to the right, and then start digging."

"That old man was kind of a joker, wasn't he?" said Josh. "Why did he have to make it such a puzzle? Seven bricks up, seven bricks over? Why couldn't he have pointed us right to the coins?"

"He was trying to make it difficult on purpose, I guess," said Bernie. "And seven is a lucky number."

"This is the right one," said Josh as he counted bricks. "It looks like it'll be pretty easy to chip away at this stuff. Let's get going!"

They set down their backpacks, got out the expandable shovel and pick, and went to work.

"We better do this as quickly as we can," said Bernie. "It'll be light in less than an hour."

"Give me the pick. I got this," said Josh. "This'll be fun," he said as he lifted the pickax.

Bernie, still nervous, looked around and into the distance. "The security detail doesn't come on until seven. We have plenty of time until then. But even so, we don't want anyone seeing us out here. Let me know when you need me to start using the shovel."

Bernie and Josh worked as quickly as they could, but the earth was packed hard and was more difficult to dislodge than they had expected. Even though the weather was cool, they were both covered in sweat before long. At last, Josh, using the pick, connected with a section of dirt that easily gave way. They had hit an empty space, a little cave-like opening. Stale air rushed out as Josh used the pick to cut the opening a little wider.

"Hey! We've got something! There's actually a hole in the wall here. Bernie, this might be it!" Josh threw down the pick and excitedly reached into the opening.

Bernie's fatigue gave way to excitement that matched Josh's. "Can you feel anything? Can you reach farther in?"

"Yeah. It goes back a little way." Josh shoved his arm in all the way up to his shoulder. "Hey, hey, Bernie! I've got something! I've got something!"

Josh pulled his arm out of the hole in the wall with something in his hand. Could it be that the ancient coins really existed? That they had been hidden away for so many hundreds of years and were finally found? Bernie shined the flashlight on the object in Josh's hand.

Later, Josh would say that Bernie was the one who screamed like a little girl while Bernie insisted it was Josh. Regardless of whose yell was more high-pitched, however, Josh dropped the thing in his hand like a hot potato.

It was a human skull.

Ancient skulls and bones, hidden for centuries in the Great Wall

"Oh my God, oh my God, oh my God," was all Josh could say as he stared at it.

"Wow. I mean, wow," was Bernie's contribution to the discussion. "Is that what I think it is?" "If you think it's a skull, then yes, I believe that's what you think it is," whispered Josh.

"What's a skull doing inside the Great Wall of China?"

Bernie explained. "I read about this. When the wall was being built, a lot of workers died in the process. Legend has it that their bodies were just tossed into the wall. Some of the workers were convicts who had been taken out of prisons and nobody cared about giving them a proper burial. It was a terrible way to treat people." Bernie tried to see the expression on Josh's face. He shined the flashlight into his cousin's eyes. "Hey, you're not too freaked out about this, are you? The coins could still be in there, you know."

"No, I'm not freaked out," said Josh, squinting. "I just want to give you a turn looking for the coins. Go ahead; stick your arm in there. I'll hold your tablet."

Bernie grimaced, but he handed Josh the tablet and stepped to the opening in the wall. He took a deep breath and reached his arm in.

"I'm not finding anything. I don't know, maybe there's—" Bernie stopped.

"What? Did you find the—"

"Nope," said Bernie with a sigh. "This does not feel like a gold coin," he said as he pulled out a handful of bones and carefully set them on the ground. "Take a look in there with your flashlight. See if you can spot anything that looks like coins. I don't want to pull out any more bones or skulls."

Josh aimed the flashlight in the hole and tried to peer in. "There are more bones, but that's all I see," he said. "Wow. What a way to die."

"Let's put these back in," said Bernie. "These people didn't get respect when they were alive, but we can at least put their remains back in their final resting place."

The two young men carefully replaced the skull and the bones in the wall. Their excitement tapered off and was replaced with fatigue as they shoveled dirt back into the hole and tried to put the crumbling bricks back where they had found them. Josh wiped his grimy forehead with an equally dirty hand.

"So, no coins. I guess it was just a story after all." He sighed as he leaned back against the wall and slid to the ground. Bernie sat next to him and put his head in his hands. The sky was starting to lighten in the distance. Everything around them looked gray, and their mood matched the surroundings.

Neither of them said anything for a few minutes. Then Bernie raised his head. "No," he said.

"Huh?" grunted Josh.

"No!" repeated Bernie, standing up. "You dragged me all the way to China and I'm not giving up now. We're going to keep digging. Come on! Let's be relentless. Let's hammer on this wall until we find those coins!"

"OK, boss. You talked me into it. Let's hydrate first, though, all right?" said Josh, still leaning against the bricks.

Josh and Bernie search for the coins, with Chen Mara and Chen Li close behind

Bernie reached over and pulled a water bottle from the backpack. He took a swig and was about to hand it to Josh when he heard a noise. Josh heard it too and looked up. It was shouts, in Chinese. They saw a small figure come over the hill toward them, running.

"Is that a security guard?" asked Josh, quickly standing up.

Bernie squinted into the distance. "I don't know," he said. "But maybe we better pack up our stuff and get away from this part of the wall."

"Sounds like a plan," agreed Josh. The figure was getting closer and was still yelling. "Wish we knew Chinese," he added as he bent over to gather the tools.

"I'm glad we don't. That person sounds pretty mad. Come on, hand me the backpack. I've got the shovel folded up."

Josh stood up and stretched. "Give me a second. My back is killing me."

Bernie saw a second person appear over the crest of the hill. Then the first person stopped and raised both hands in a position Bernie was familiar with from all the times he'd ridden along with his father on his police beat.

"Josh! Get down!" Bernie dove at his cousin and knocked him to the ground as a shot rang out. A bullet sank into the crumbling brick right above where Josh's head had been a moment ago.

"Oof!" said Josh as he hit the ground. "That was a gunshot!"

The person who shot at them was now close enough for them to see. "Isn't that Chen Li's mother?" asked Josh in surprise. Bernie looked past Chen Mara at the person who had appeared behind her.

"Mother, stop!" she cried. "Please, stop!"

"Chen Li? What are you doing here?" Bernie called out as he scrambled to his feet.

Confident that she had gotten their attention with her first shot, Chen Mara walked slowly and deliberately toward Bernie and Josh. Chen Li ran past her.

"Bernie! Josh! Are you all right?" she asked Josh, who was still on the ground.

"Yeah." Josh brushed himself off and looked around in a daze. He hadn't been shot at since the old days in L.A. It sure wasn't something he missed.

Chen Li turned to Bernie. "My mother was determined to follow you. I came with her to stop her in case she tried to—to hurt you."

Before they could say any more, Chen Mara spoke.

"I will kill you if I must," she said coldly as she walked forward, brandishing the gun. "Have you found the coins? Give them to me."

"No, ma'am, Mrs. Chen," said Bernie evenly, holding up his hands as if to show her their search had been fruitless. "We didn't find the coins. It won't do any good to shoot at us. It's no use wasting our time over this. The coins aren't there."

"It must've been a hoax," said Josh. "We dug a hole in the wall right here, where it said to on the map. All we found were bones."

Chen Mara desperately reaches for her heart's desire

Chen Mara screamed as the pickax hit air. She threw the tool aside and dug at the opening with her bare hands, like a starving animal scrabbling for food, fueled by the adrenaline of bitterness and greed. Clawing at the opening in the wall, she paid no attention to her bleeding hands and broken fingernails. All her senses were consumed by the fulfillment of her lifelong desire. The gold coins, the riches, the wealth that her family had dreamed about for generations, was almost in her grasp. Nothing was going to stop her now.

Tears streamed down Chen Li's face as she watched Chen Mara in her frenzy. She wanted to scream, but she could barely speak above a whisper. "Please, please, Mother. Don't do this to yourself."

Bernie put his arm around her shoulder. Josh glanced at Bernie, but didn't speak. He shook his head and then looked back at the wall. Amazingly, Chen Mara had dug an opening big enough to squeeze her gaunt body into.

"I can smell them! I can feel them! I know they are here!" she said as she squeezed her head and shoulders into the hole. Her muffled voice came from inside the wall. "I can see them! I can see them!"

"She's gone crazy," said Josh. "She thinks she sees the coins!"

"Let's try to get her out of there. She's going to need medical attention," said Bernie. "Stay here, Chen Li. We'll get her out without hurting her."

"Hopefully without us getting hurt, either," muttered Josh under his breath. "She's nuts."

As Josh and Bernie started toward the wall, something flew out toward them. Josh's first impulse was to duck. Now what was happening? The object fell a few feet from where they were standing. Bernie moved to pick it up.

"She did see them," he said in amazement as he held up a small, heavy parcel. It was a leather pouch tied shut by a drawstring. He handed it to Chen Li. She loosened the drawstring. Onto the ground tumbled five heavy gold disks, about the size of her palm, each wrapped in leather.

"The coins!" said Chen Li, looking down at them in amazement. "They are real!"

The three looked up again as they heard four heavy thuds on the ground in quick succession. Chen Mara, still inside the wall, was tossing out more bags of coins. She was still yelling, her voice becoming hoarse and broken.

Six, then seven, eight, nine bags. Forty ancient gold coins lay on the ground in front of the hole in the Great Wall of China. Coins that had not seen the light of day since 1640. Coins that had been hidden by a wise old man—because of their great value? Or because of the potential for greed and selfishness that accompanied them?

Josh and Bernie stared at the coins on the ground, shocked into silence. Chen Li pulled her gaze away and called, "Mother, please come out! Please! Everything is going to be all right now!"

If Chen Mara heard her daughter, she did not respond. All her attention was on the coins. When she first crawled inside the wall, Chen Mara could barely reach the bags of coins, and when she did grasp the first one, it didn't budge. The bags were tangled up in roots that had grown around them. She had to claw and dig with all her might to free them. In her desperation to free the coins, she pulled away almost an entire ceiling of root growth, and the weakened earth began to collapse.

Chen Li called again. "Mother! Come out!"

Chen Mara called back, speaking in Chinese. "I have to get all the coins. I have to get all my riches! There's one more bag! I can't get it loose!"

Grasping and pulling at the last roots holding the earth above her, Chen Mara pulled her body all the way into the wall and yanked at the remaining bag of coins.

"*Suǒyǒu shuí cóng wǒ de cáifù shǐ wǒ!*" (You who have kept me from my riches!)

Breathing in the ancient dust, she coughed and choked.

"*Wǒ zǔzhòu nǐ!*" (I curse you!)

Finally, the crumbling bricks and the earth above the small cave began to give way. The wall above Chen Mara was disintegrating. Josh yelled out, "The wall! It's starting to collapse! Mrs. Chen!"

Chen Li ran to the opening. "*Māmā, māmā, zǒuchū!*" (Mother, Mother, get out!)

"*Wú! Wǒ bìxū yǒngyǒu zhè yīqiè!*" (No! I must have it all!) came the cry from inside. With one final desperate grab, Chen Mara freed the last bag of coins, and loosened the rest of the ceiling of roots and earth.

"*Wǒ yǒu tā! Zhè shì zài wǒ de shǒu!*" (I have it! It's in my hand!) she shrieked as the falling bricks began to block the opening.

Now she had everything. Now she would live her life as she deserved, a rich woman. "*Shènglì! Zhōngyú, zhōngyú!*" (Victory! At last, at last!) She choked out the words as her mouth filled with debris and dirt.

Twisting her body around and pushing with her legs, Chen Mara desperately tried to find a way out of the hole that was closing around her. Darkness and dust were everywhere. Blinking, her eyes streaming with tears, she saw a small shaft of light and pulled herself toward it. The bricks and earth were still falling, soon to completely obliterate the hole in the wall. Now desperate to get out but barely able to move, she wrenched forward a few more inches, just reaching what was left of the opening.

Outside, Bernie and Josh grabbed the pickax and shovel. Chen Li stood by, weeping. They saw Chen Mara's arm emerge from what remained of the opening, clinging to the bag of coins she was so desperate to have. Before they could attempt to pull her out, the final crash of bricks and earth blocked any hope of rescue, leaving only Chen Mara's hand and wrist visible from beneath the pile of rubble. Josh rushed forward with the pickax while Bernie held a sobbing Chen Li. "Mama, Mama," she cried softly.

Josh beat at the collapsed wall as hard as he could. "We've got to get her out!" he yelled. He managed to move some dirt around Chen Mara's hand, but for every inch he cleared, more rocks and earth fell. After a few minutes, dropping the pickax in frustration, he knelt down and lifted Chen Mara's wrist to feel for a pulse. Nothing. Her limp hand felt cold. Josh felt a chill run through him as well. "Mrs. Chen!" he whispered.

He glanced up at Bernie, who had been watching intently, Chen Li's face still buried in his shoulder. Josh shook his head. "I think she's—". Bernie nodded in understanding, and held up his hand to keep Josh from finishing the sentence.

The end of Chen Mara's sad, selfish life

338

Josh looked down again at the dead woman's hand. The drawstring on the last bag of coins was still tangled around her limp fingers. You lived a miserable life, he thought. You put your daughter through so much grief, too. And for what? Money's not everything. "And believe me, lady," he muttered to himself as he took the bag from her cold hand and stood up. "You won't be needing this where you're going."

Josh touched the "contact emergency services" button on his comm and turned to look at the sky. The sun was rising, casting a warm light over the wall, but the air was still chilly. He walked back to where the boys had left the spare backpack they had brought in case the coins were found. He gathered up the leather bags and placed them in the pack, holding onto the last one for a moment, the one that had sealed Chen Mara's fate and caused her death. With a sigh, he dropped it in with the others, and zipped the heavy pack shut. Then he sat down on the grass and watched the sun rise as it slowly shed its light on the scene at Simatai: A young man comforting a sobbing young woman, another young man sitting thoughtfully on the ground, and at the wall, the end of a journey for an angry, bitter woman. For her, the wall was not the treasure trove of riches that she had dreamed of hoarding, but a pile of rubble that became her grave.

to Simatai with Bernie, an American tourist who was staying at their hotel. They had been hiking at the wall when they discovered an opening in the deteriorating bricks, and Chen Mara became greatly distressed. She had heard stories that some of her ancestors were buried inside the wall. She crawled inside hoping to find remains. They tried to stop her, but she was buried in a sudden cave-in. Chen Li's hands shook as she told the story to the police. Bernie stood by her side, almost holding her up.

The paramedics arrived to remove Chen Mara's remains from the rubble. Chen Li asked to be taken to the police station for the rest of the interview. She could not bear to see her mother's body. Bernie went with her, still supporting the shaking girl. After another few hours of questioning, they were released, and Josh answered Bernie's call, arriving in the shuttle bus to take them back to the hotel.

The boys were concerned about Chen Li, but they were also anxious to contact their family back home as they had promised. Late that afternoon, Chen Li was finally able to rest for a few hours. While she was sleeping, Bernie set up a three-way video call between them, New York and Los Angeles. The boys agreed to hold back on the news that they had been shot at and a woman had died. For now, they would only tell the good stuff.

After the greetings, Matt was first to ask. "How about it? Did you find the coins?"

Josh could see Leah in the background, telling Meg that Daddy was on the comm. "Hi sweetie!" he said, waving, as Leah held her up. "I'll be home soon!"

"Dad, it's almost unbelievable," said Bernie, answering Matt's question. "The map was real! We found the coins in the Great Wall. There's fifty of them, exactly as the map described!"

There was silence for a moment on the other end. Bernie thought they had lost the audio connection. "Dad? Mom? Can you hear me?"

Suddenly everyone talked at once. ""I knew it!" yelled Matt. "It's the magic of the life chest!"

"Really? They're really real? And they're real gold?" asked Leah excitedly.

"Did you take pictures? Send them right now!" said Catherine. "Hold one of the coins up to the screen; I want to see what they look like!" Bernie obliged.

Ruby said, "I'm so proud of you both! The coins are amazing. Mr. CC's family will be thrilled!"

"Josh, you really did it!" said Leah. "I love you, Babe!" She turned to her little daughter. "What, sweetie? Oh, okay. Josh, Meg wants you to bring her a toy tiger!"

"Will do," said Josh, laughing. "This whole trip has been beyond belief. We've got a lot more to tell when we get back. Let's just say it's been unforgettable in a lot of ways." He turned to his cousin. "Hey, Bernie might have some special news. Remember when he described his ideal girl and put the list in his life chest, ten years ago? She's real, too!"

Bernie's face became almost as red as his hair. He turned away from the comm and whispered anxiously, "Josh! Don't tell them yet!"

"Tell them what?" asked Josh with an innocent smile.

Bernie turned back to the comm screen. "Hey folks, I guess we better go now," he said, trying to sound casual.

"Wait a minute!" said his mom. "You met a girl? Oh, Bernie! That's wonderful!"

"I'm gonna get that note out of your life chest, son!" teased Matt. "Let's see now. I think you wanted a girl who was smart, had a nice smile and honest eyes. Somebody who didn't play games."

"That's right, Dad," Bernie confessed. "I think I may have found her."

"Yes!" Matt fist-pumped the air. "I'm telling you, it's the magic of the life chest!"

"So why don't you go on down and spend some more time with her before we have to leave?"

"I wish I could. I don't think I can be with her another half hour without telling her that I love her. But like I said, it's not the right time. This is a terrible tragedy she's dealing with. Her whole life has been upended. I can't ask her to think about me while she's just beginning to grieve for her mother." Bernie went to the closet for his suitcase. "So let's get this room cleaned up and get ready to go to Thailand. We're about to make some people we don't even know very, very happy."

The next day was like any other for the Chen family in Bangkok, until that evening when two young American strangers came to their door. Bernie and Josh tried to explain the whole story before they actually produced the coins. There were a few false starts and misunderstandings, but there were enough family members who spoke English to help translate successfully. The only person who didn't quite understand that Josh and Bernie were not Mormon missionaries was Chen Mara's uncle, who besides not being able to speak any English was also quite deaf.

"*Nǐ shuō shénme?*" (What did you say?) he interjected every other sentence, along with "*Dàshēng shuōhuà!*" (Talk louder!)

The old uncle was talking to his wife with his back to Josh and Bernie when they pulled the first bag of coins out of the backpack. The old auntie fainted, collapsing into her nephew's arms. Her husband began to scold her for falling asleep in front of guests, and then turned around. When he saw what had caused her to faint, he staggered too, and was helped to a chair by Bernie.

After everyone had recovered, the rest of the day was filled with celebration and reminiscing. Bernie and Josh got to see for themselves the family chests that had inspired their great-great-grandpa Kim. They were speechless when the old uncle opened the lid of the Dynasty chest, the chest that had been built by Marco Polo and had once held the fifty gold coins. It was like a dream to finally see it.

Mr. CC's family gets a big surprise

Bernie and Josh stayed overnight with Chen Li's Bangkok family. They wanted to take the time to explain the situation involving Chen Mara and Chen Li and the fact that the joy of finding the coins was tempered by the tragedy of Chen Mara's death.

The old uncle called the entire family, including Josh and Bernie, to the dining room the next morning. Everyone took their places around the table and the old uncle sat in his chair at the head, the gold coins arranged on a lacquered tray in front of him. He spoke in Chinese and his nephew interpreted in English for Josh and Bernie.

"Young men," he began. "You are honorable representatives of your family. Your ancestors are proud, and we are grateful. I have a great responsibility now to see that this legacy is used wisely. Part of it belongs to you. Your ancestor kept the map, and kept the story alive. You took up the quest and were successful. As I said, we are grateful. We would be honored to have you share in these riches." He picked up a stack of five coins and handed them to Josh. "These are for you." He handed another stack to Bernie. "And you."

Bernie and Chen Li plan for the future

Bernie reached out and took her hand. "You're free," he said. "You can make your life anything you want it to be."

"I do know that I will open my family's chests. They won't be hidden away any longer with me as the keeper. And I will have my own life chest built. I want it to be a symbol of hope, and of a happy future, like your life chests are. But—" she paused. "I don't know what my future will be. I may visit the family in Thailand, since I have no other relatives here in China. I'd like to go to university. And you, Bernie—"

"Don't worry about me, Chen Li. I'll be there for you no matter what you decide," said Bernie, holding Chen Li's small hand in both of his.

"Yeah, I think you're stuck with him," Josh laughed. "I suppose you could've done worse. Hey, you get me in the bargain. This guy and I are joined at the hip."

"Right. Love me, love my cousin? Well, tolerate my cousin, anyway," Bernie grinned.

Chen Li looked at Bernie. "I am happy," she said in the honest, open way that he loved so much. "It has changed my life, meeting you."

She reached across the table and took Josh's hand with her free one. "Both of you," she smiled.

A lifetime of love- predicted by a note in Bernie's life chest!

Epilogue

A Life Chest Legacy for April

"Grandpa, what's your favorite flavor of ice cream?" asked April as she licked her cone. It was summer again. April and Josh had walked to the ice cream parlor a few blocks from Meg's. Meg was getting a new floor cleaning system put in and Josh said he'd come over and get April out of her hair. His granddaughter was almost nine years old now, and she was as rambunctious—and curious—as Josh had been at that age.

Grandpa Josh and April share ice cream and life chest stories

"I don't know, Blossom," answered Josh. "When I'm eating strawberry, then it's strawberry. But when I'm eating pistachio, then it's pistachio. If I grab your cone and finish it off, then it'll be chocolate. It's a problem."

"It's not a problem, because I'm not giving you my cone," April said matter-of-factly as she popped the last bite into her mouth. "You had a vanilla one. Besides, Grandma said you should eat less ice cream."

"Oh, she did? Aw, she just never forgot the time I won that bet with Bernie and ate three gallons in one sitting. It was fudge ripple, by the way. Fudge ripple isn't my favorite anymore."

"Oh, Grandpa, you're silly."

"You don't believe me?" Josh put a hand to his heart, pretending to be shocked. "We can call up Uncle Bernie right now and ask him."

"I don't want to ask him about that. I want to ask him about the coins."

"The coins?"

"The story you were telling me this morning about the coins that you found in China, when Great-Uncle Bernie met Aunt Li. I want to ask him if that story is true."

"Well, it's the middle of the night where they are, Blossom. You're just going to have to take my word for it."

"So it is true, Grandpa? You really found fifty gold coins in the Great Wall of China?" Josh chuckled. "It was a great story, wasn't it?"

"It's the best. Grandpa, I want to grow up to be like you and Great-Uncle Bernie. I want to have adventures, and take pictures, and write journals, and put all my memories in my life chest." April bounced up and down in her chair. Her eyes shone at the thought of all the adventures she planned to have.

"That's great, Blossom. That's what the life chest stories are for. Doesn't matter if they're true or not, just that they get you excited about filling your own life chest, right?"

"I guess so, Grandpa." April stood up. "Can I get another ice cream cone? I want black cherry this time."

"Well, a small one," answered Josh.

"Aw, Grandpa. Grandma didn't say *I* had to eat less ice cream."

"We haven't had dinner yet, Blossom. A small cone." Josh reached into his pocket for the bank card that he handed to April.

"Okay. Thanks." April skipped to the counter. Josh stood up to stretch and then put his hand back in his jacket pocket. His fingers closed around a disk. A heavy, worn, gold-colored coin that he always carried with him. It reminded him of the past, helped him appreciate the present—and looking at his granddaughter skipping back toward him—gave him hope for the future.

An ancient gold coin; an astounding legacy

— Appendix A —

Learnings Guide

Valuable learnings woven throughout The Life Chest story,
derived from the Pumptitude Trilogy

#	Learning	Chapter	Character
1	**POWER OF AND**	**Prologue**	**Josh**
2	**EMBRACE THE PRINCIPAL OF KAIZEN**	**Prologue**	**Matt & Josh**
3	**GET VERTICAL**	**Prologue**	**Matt & Josh**
4	**THINK ABUNDANTLY**	**1**	**Niccolo & Marco Polo**
5	**CUT YOUR LOSSES**	**1**	**Marco Polo, Gurmi & The Porters**
6	**SEE INTO THE FUTURE**	**1**	**Gurmi**
7	**MENTOR**	**1**	**Marco Polo & Gurmi**

#	Learning	Chapter	Character
8	SUCCESS HAS NO SHORTCUTS	3	Liu Li Yong & Liu Shen
9	TRUST EVERYONE	3	Liu Li Yong & Liu Li Jun
10	BE OPEN FOR LEARNING	4	Liu Li Yong
11	FACE YOUR FEARS	5	Liu Zhang Wei & Xiun Ai
12	RECOGNIZE YOUR DEFINING MOMENTS	5	Liu Zhang Wei
13	HOLD YOURSELF ACCOUNTABLE	5	Liu Zhang Wei & Liu Li Jun
14	TAP INTO THE WISDOM OF REFLECTION	5	Liu Li Yong & Liu Li Jun
15	DO WHAT OTHER PEOPLE WILL NOT DO	6	Liu Zhang Wei

#	Learning	Chapter	Character
16	**LEAVE A LEGACY**	**6**	**Liu Zhang Wei**
17	**KNOW WHO YOU CAN COUNT ON**	**6**	**Liu Zhang Wei & Xiun Ai**
18	**FACE FEAR**	**6**	**Liu Zhang Wei & Xun Ai**
19	**KEEP IT FIGGY**	**7**	**Liu Zhang Wei & Liu Li Juan**
20	**LIFES BIGGEST CHALLENGE**	**8**	**Sun Wang Min**
21	**FOCUS: KILL THE WAR LORD**	**8**	**Wang Zhang Yong**
22	**CHECK YOUR EGO AT THE DOOR**	**8**	**Sun Zhang Lei**
23	**ONE WORD**	**9**	**Wu Li Ming**

#	Learning	Chapter	Character
24	CURIOSITY	9	Wang Lie Jie
25	STEP OUT OF YOUR COMFORT ZONE	9	Wang Liu Yang
26	PICK WHAT SWORDS TO DIE ON	10	Chen Liu Wei & Chen Mogwai
27	FIND HEAVEN ON EARTH	10	Chen Wang Ping
28	BEWARE OF ENERGY VAMPIRES	10	Wu Wang Xiu Lan
29	GATHER YOUR MEMORIES	10	Marco Polo & Kublai Khan
30	LET GO OF WHAT YOU CAN'T CHANGE	10	Chen Liu Wei & Chen Mogwai
31	ATTITUDE DETERMINES ALTITUDE	11	Josh & April

#	Learning	Chapter	Character
32	PERFORM WELL AT WORK	12	Bill & Kim
33	CHOOSE YOUR OWN SHMONDAY	12	Kim & Ashley
34	LEARN TO THINK OUTSIDE THE BOX	12	Josh & April
35	ESTABLISH YOUR CORE VALUES	12	Ashley
36	WALK WITH PURPOSE	12	Josh & April
37	SAY YES TO THE CHEST	12	Ashley & Noah
38	NO REGRETS	12	Noah
39	TAKE A POWER NAP	12	Meg & Kim

With one family the course of the Dynasty Chest is altered:

7. Liu Shen
Father of the Old Man
Spirit

8. Liu Li Yong
The Old Man
Brave

9. Liu Li Jun
The Older Brother
Army

At the time of his death, Liu Li Jun passes on the Dynasty Chest to his younger brother Liu Zhang Wei.

Liu Zhang Wei keeps safe the Dynasty Chest and creates his own chest, the War Chest.

From then on, each time the chests are passed on, a new chest is also created.

Liu Zhang Wei
The Younger Brother
Great
1. Dynasty Chest
2. War Chest

Liu Li Juan
Beautiful
3. Blossom Chest

Sun Zhang Lei
Rock Pile
4. Forbidden City Chest

Sun Wang Min
Quick
5. Contentment Chest

Wang Zhang Yong
Brave
6. Centering Chest

Wang Lie Jie
Hero
7. Curiosity Chest

Wang Liu Yang
Ocean
8. Challenge Chest

Wu Li Ming
Bright
9. Calligraphy Chest

Wu Wang Xiu Lan
Elegant Orchid
10. Chest Of Words

Chen Wang Ping
Mr. CCs Grandfather
Peaceful
11. Bamboo Chest

Chen Liu Wei
Mr. CCs Father
Great
12. Yin Yang Chest

Chen Cheng Gong	**Chen Mogwai**
Mr. CC	Mr. CCs Brother
Success	Evil
13. Abundance Chest	1. Creates his own Chest
Mr. CC's Son	Chen Jin
	Money
Mr. CC's Granddaughter	Chen Bao
	Treasure
Mr. CC's Great Grandson	Chen Jun
	Supreme
Mr. CC's Great Great Grandson	Chen Mara
	Evil
Mr. CC's Great Great Great Grandson	Chen Li
	Reason

Mr. CC gives the map to Kim Yost, who is inspired to create his own chest and later a business called The Life Chest.

As the Life Chests are passed on through the generations, each member of Chen Mogwai's family is told the story of the map.

Kim Yost
1. Marco Polo Chest

Ashley Yost
2. Havana Chest

Noah
3. New Yorker Chest

Ruby
Bernie's Mother
4. Salzburg Chest

Catherine
Josh's Mother
1. Salzburg Chest

Bernie
5. Pirate Chest

Josh
2. Pirate Chest

April
Josh's Granddaughter
3. Zen Blossom Chest

— Appendix D —
Photo Album

THE LIFE CHEST